# LONGER LIFE,
# MORE JOY

# LONGER LIFE, MORE JOY

## Techniques for Enhancing Health, Happiness and Inner Vision

**Gay Gaer Luce**

NEWCASTLE PUBLISHING CO., INC.
North Hollywood, California
1992

Edited by Karen Westerberg Reyes and Lorena Fletcher Farrell
Cover Design by Michele Lanci-Altomare

First Edition April 1992

The material contained in *Longer Life, More Joy* is not meant to substitute for your physician's advice; it should complement it. Any health and lifestyle recommendations presented herein should be followed only after consulting with your doctor.

A Newcastle Book
First Printing April 1992
9  8  7  6  5  4  3  2  1
Printed in the United States of America

This book is dedicated to my mother and father and the mysterious source of their truth, love and wisdom.

# CONTENTS

# INTRODUCTION

In January 1974, a group of twelve adventuresome older people (ages 63 through 77) met with four younger people to explore the myths and realities of the aging process. The group called itself SAGE, an acronym for Senior Actualization and Growth Explorations. This experimental program continued for more than ten years and its offshoots are active today. By word of mouth many new people came to SAGE, people of all ages who hoped to become re-excited about life—like falling in love again. Their experiences opened them up to their own sense of aliveness, to unforeseen possibilities for their lives and new styles of being. The discoveries were so startling that similar programs began across the country and eventually spread to other parts of the world. What we in that group discovered about the possibilities and excitements of old age provides the contents of this book.

## MY STORY

In 1971 I was a disillusioned science writer. I wanted to give my readers something more. I began to explore hypnosis, yoga and other ways I thought might help people improve their own health and well-being. As I began to understand them I wished I had learned the techniques as a child. They would have changed my life and made it freer, less neurotic and more pleasurable. Then it occurred to me that I might try teaching children these simple practices.

While I was developing the skills needed to convey this knowledge to children my mother came to visit me. As we spent time together I realized these were skills that might be valuable to her, as well. For instance, she was having a hard time falling asleep. I thought if I could teach her to relax at will she could fall asleep more quickly. Using biofeedback skills I taught her she found it amazingly easy to visualize a spiral vortex through which she would travel out into sleep. That excited her interest. Next she learned some yoga breathing and she amazed me by holding her breath to a count of 100.

What she had learned about control became even more apparent a month later when she was involved in a head-on automobile collision during which she remained calm and cool by practicing her breathing techniques. An 18-year-old in diabetic shock, fleeing the police, came at her going about 35 miles an hour the wrong way down a one-way street. They collided at a combined speed of 90 miles an hour. Yet Mother was totally calm when the ambulance arrived, and, despite her age and vulnerability because of injuries received in a previous accident, left the hospital before the 18-year-old. She was then convinced more than ever of the power of her mind and ready for more new experiences.

The next step was to offer her a transcendent experience through a technique that involves lying comfortably on a couch, relaxing, and listening to music through earphones until reaching a trance-like state.

My mother, who was 71 at the time, is a rare woman, a fine artist, and an intellectual with great curiosity. I wondered if her new adventures and changes were purely signs of her own unusual character or whether some of these experiences would have the same effect on other older people. At the time centers of gerontology were not that interested in transcendent experience in older people, in their special abilities, or in preparation for death. Most gerontological literature was concerned mainly with the limitations of age, decline of abilities and loss of strength and energy. I could not bring myself to believe that growing old, a completely natural happening, could be so joyless. There had been too many remarkable older people: Joseph Campbell, Pablo Casals, Buckminster Fuller, Maggie Kuhn, Margaret Mead, Georgia O'Keefe, Pablo Picasso, Bertrand Russell, Frank Lloyd Wright—older people who were full of vitality and spicy wisdom.

What did it take to grow old like them? What indeed does it take to grow?

In early childhood everyone is expected to grow. Children are offered challenges. They are held, hugged, nurtured and made comfortable in their being, always exploring their worth through a deep tactile contact with others. We usually undervalue the importance of affection and contact in learning, and touching virtually stops in early adulthood. Compared with an adult, a child is in constant motion. And no one is surprised if he or she makes odd sounds for hours, makes funny faces in the mirror, plays roles, talks to imaginary playmates, stands on his or her head, leaps and rolls and chortles, or whirls in circles to experience dizziness. Nobody is surprised because he or she is growing. A child doesn't have to be self-conscious—we all know that free play is how a child grows.

Wouldn't we grow at any age if we had similar freedom and support? But the stereotypes of our culture say:

Old people should be dignified and circumspect.

Old dogs can't learn new tricks.

Old people are closed-minded, set in their way, slow, senile.
Old people are ugly.
There is no future for old people. Why teach them?
Old people don't want to use or touch their bodies.
Old people like to sit still and be quiet.

I didn't believe these negative propositions, nor did my friends.
We decided then and there to experiment. If we created something
like the situation in which children grow, wouldn't we all grow?

## AN UNEASY ROAD

After a year of discouraging library research I gave up, hoping
someone else would point the way. I enrolled in a summerlong
program with a powerful and learned Tibetan lama, Rinpoche
Tarthang Tulku, and was introduced to extraordinary psychological and spiritual practices more than a thousand years old. In that
same program were two women who wanted to try these methods
with older people. Carole Spencer had studied the problems of
aging for her doctoral dissertation in psychology, but she was less
interested in aging pathology than in meditation, Tai Chi and the
possibilities of spiritual development. Susan Garfield, a documen-
tary filmmaker at the time, was also attracted by the possibilities
of service and spiritual development.

But the project really began to take shape when I met Eugenia
Gerrard. Her mother was dying of Alzheimer's disease and Eugenia was profoundly interested in all the dynamics of aging. An
intense person with a Texas accent and formidable strength, she
brought with her a background that included training in breath-
work, dance therapy and, later, family therapy. She worked

mainly out of her moment-by-moment feelings, sharing her love and her own problems as she taught people the methods that had been helpful in her life.

Kenneth Dychtwald arrived several months later. He was young, bristling with energy and humor, and fresh from leading yoga and body therapies at Esalen. Ken was imbued with an eagerness to change the negative image he himself had previously had of aging. Working behind the scenes was healer-psychotherapist Erik Peper. He and I had experimented with biofeedback as a way of training people to heal themselves of illnesses like colitis and hypertension. He was currently working on the theory that migraine headaches, asthma, arthritis and many other ailments could be relieved or even eliminated through the use of this learning therapy. In addition, I had discovered that some of the ancient Tibetan Buddhist practices (embracing the purpose of laying a path for wholeness in a well-defined spiritual sense) had a surface resemblance to bioenergetics, Reichian therapy, and other mind-body therapies. These exercises and visualizations had blown my own world wide open; and so, although my experience with them was skimpy, they became my tools, along with Western relaxation methods.

We were on our way.

## STARTING PREMISES

The following premises were the bulwark of our new movement:

**There is a purpose to old age:** a future to be fulfilled. Rinpoche Tarthang Tulku said, "The first part of life is for learning, the second for service, and the last for oneself." It is a time to discover inner richness for self-development and spiritual growth. It is also a time of transition and preparation for dying, which is at least as important as preparation for a career or family. Out of this time of inner growth come our sages, healers, prophets, and models for the generations to follow.

**People need special conditions for deep growth:** affirmation, challenge, guidance, stimulation, encouragement, support, deep emotional nourishment, and permission to be un-self-conscious—to be themselves. These conditions are as necessary for older people as for children.

**Growth and well-being are enhanced by increasing pleasurable experience.** Rather than dwelling on problems and negative feelings, older people need to experience magnificent alternative ways of being, new facets of themselves, new ways of exploring and controlling their minds and bodies so that old problems recede and dissolve.

**Each person is unique and will unfold in his or her own way.** A smorgasbord of techniques should be available so each person can choose those that suit him or her best.

**No one can be compared with anyone else.** Each person's odyssey of development will be different, and so each person must be carefully listened to and supported through his or her particular needs and quirks until he or she finds the best way to unfold.

**Older people may develop faster than young people in certain respects.** Older people have an experienced wisdom that young people haven't acquired. They also have less investment in ego, since they are no longer creating a career or raising a family, and this may give them the freedom to adopt new attitudes and lifestyles.

**Many of the ailments of age are reversible.** Many chronic symptoms appear as the result of long-term reactions to stress, along with generally poor diet and a sedentary life. After a person learns relaxation methods to "un-stress," many symptoms begin to diminish and he or she can regain vitality.

**Our thoughts and attitudes create our feelings and shape our bodies and lives.** Although we shape much of what we experience in life, we do not discover this source of control and creativity until we are well along in life and have developed countless beliefs and habits that are not even conscious—such as the way we sit down in a chair or respond when someone uses language we don't like. The fact that we are unconscious of the way we sit down or form preferences does not mean we have no underlying attitudes. Growth is the process of making these hidden components of ourselves conscious.

**Old age can be a time of emancipation from the inhibitions and habits learned in childhood.** From early in life all of us absorbed social amenities; we learned to be nice or put up with boring situations or make stern moral judgments on the "other" half of the world. Old age can be a time of emancipation from these constricting social customs and views.

**Old age can be a time of truth.** All things are transitory—human relationships, nations, the stock market, and life itself. Even the sun and stars are in transition. To grow old is to enter a major transition; the closer we come to death the closer we come to reality and truth. Usually we are forbidden to talk about this, although it is the human condition. But the more openly we can share this transition, the more we can accept the greater reality that is life.

Our group began with these propositions and we asked ourselves how we could construct a program that would counter the negatives, avoidances and lies—for example, that life is unending and death will never happen—we had learned so well to live with. We realized we were about to create a paradox: reality mixed with maximum pleasure.

## THE FIRST GROUP

It had been an overcast but dry January in Berkeley and the weather was chilly. We had turned the heat up in our refurbished old house and raked the leaves from the winding path outside. Eugenia, Carol and I awaited the first members of the group like teenagers waiting for the first glimpse of a blind date.

A forlorn figure with a cane, plaid cap pulled down over his eyes, limped down the path. He was shy and depressed and told us he was so old his memory no longer allowed him to recall names. For this reason he had stopped participating in church social groups. We learned later that he was only 67. He also told us his sleep was terrible and he suffered from intense tension headaches. Born in a small Western town, he had bummed on the railroads during the Depression, had ranched and gardened, and had worked for the telephone company.

A small woman bundled up in a red coat arrived and inspected the place. She asked a hundred questions about our training, credentials, and what techniques we were going to use. She was the fomenter of the program, a bristling, pert, incisive woman, certain of her rights and her opinions, competent, but feeling at the time that her life was over and that she was useless. She was 74. Her husband and lifelong companion was dying of cancer. What was left? By the time she was 76, two years later, Helen Ansley was in another city leading groups of her own and doing some writing. At 91 she had toured the country looking for a location for her "last resort," a beautiful place to die, and she had written a book: *Life's Finishing School.*

These two firstcomers were active people by temperament. They had been politically active all their lives—on opposite sides of the fence—and they fought vehemently. The others were different; some were mellower, others more private, but they were overall a gutsy group.

One woman in her mid-60s had experienced more of the "growth" movement than we had. A beautiful and inward person, she had grown weary of being the only older person in her other workshops.

There was also a tall, slender black woman who really caused us to wonder about the genetics of aging. She had a quality of wonderment and youth that made us doubt she could be in her 60s, as she told us she was. She didn't have a line in her face. Although she had suffered numerous bouts with cancer she was looking forward to going back to school to study journalism and poetry. She would graduate (at age 75) from the University of California.

Another woman, 74 years of age, said she was deeply depressed and lonely. She blamed her marriage. She was shy and had never been in a group before. After eight months with us she felt confident enough to get a divorce and move to Florida with her sister.

A sensuous and attractive man also joined us. He suffered from painful arthritis. He had been a union leader and a fighter all his life. His tension was so great that he would talk in an ordinary conversation with fists clenched. Relaxation exercises and breathing were a beginning of comfort for him. He eventually learned to accept his retirement. After a few months he began to take some of the massage and relaxation methods home to his wife, a counselor, who was so impressed with his change that she asked to join the group.

There was another woman, in her early 70s, who had been withdrawn and shy all her life. For the first five months she said almost nothing, but sat with a Mona Lisa smile as she watched the group. One day she exploded in words—saying what was on her mind, expressing her true feelings as she had never allowed herself to do before. Not too many months later she emerged as one of the group's most outspoken leaders.

A wry, handsome man, retired from the phone company, was the oldest. He was 78 and complained of stiffness and heart disease. He was shy, and only after he had been in the group for many months did we learn that he had become an artist, a poet and a master ceramist since his retirement.

One of the last to arrive was a stunning woman whose radiance suggested that she had come to teach us. Only much later did we discover that the group contributed as much to her serene composure as she did to ours.

Each member was unique and memorable. One had been a Bohemian living in a common-law marriage for 46 years at a time when that lifestyle was very unusual. Others had been in politics and unions, had been accountants, secretaries and bookkeepers. They were not leisurely people, as we imagined they might be. They were busy either with families or in the community.

That first group's age range was 63 through 77. But as SAGE grew, the range widened and embraced people as young as 32 and as old as 92.

All participants had to attend at least two sessions a week for at least six months, and spend an hour a day at home doing exercises. After all, if they were going to reverse habits and symptoms acquired over six decades or more, they were not likely to succeed unless they repeatedly did the exercises.

## OUR AIMS: HOLISM AND HEALTH

We knew that we who led the program would have to enjoy it as much as the older participants, so we worked out methods we figured would tickle or excite us too. It was not going to be a program *for them*. It was going to be *for all of us*. We decided to teach in teams. That way we could learn from each other and each leader could spend part of the time as a participant.

Only mavericks would undertake such a program. Here we were with full-time unpaid jobs, no insurance, lots of expenses, and we spent our time with old people. Our families thought we were more than a little crazy.

Mavericks tend to disagree with each other. But we agreed on our quest for a quality we called *holism*: We wanted to deal with whole people, body-mind-spirit, and not give exercises just for the ankles or eyes, or for revitalizing the memory. Holism is not a collection of techniques passed out by experts, it is an attitude and a sharing. "It is a passionate way of looking at people, not in their separateness but at their fullness," Ken Dychtwald explained. "Holistic health is a recognition that we aren't parts of who we are—not just a leg, arm, thought, or arithritic joint—not who we used to be or who we might be: We are all those things."

Having agreed that our aim was holistic we began planning a program for health. Often we even battled over what health meant. We knew it was not simply a given quality that was taken away by age: It had to be part of a process of living. Health is freedom—

from pain, disability, emotional hang-ups and mental confusion. Our culture teaches us many ways to be unhealthy; we get the message from the junk-food sellers and the violent programs on TV. We are taught in first grade to stop feeling who we are ("You can stand in the hall if you're going to cry"), and to give up our lives for good grades, reputation and, later, money. Many of us have lived like speed demons, striving to keep up with other people's expectations and ideas about life.

Out of ignorance about the basics of health we abuse and neglect ourselves for 50 or 60 years and then react with indignation, surprise or grief when we find ourselves with intractable ailments, aches and stiffness. Life is movement. City life is mostly sedentary. Look at the child—restless, ever in motion, always growing, grasping, tumbling upside down, expressing feelings freely and exploring. Then he or she goes to school where this dynamic body is forced to sit as motionless as possible for eight hours a day. After we leave school, we start working. We relax with beer and television. Golf on Sunday. We watch movies, play cards, watch baseball. Talk. We learn a pattern of ever-greater closing up, quieting down. The less we move the less we feel the need to move. Breathing less deeply in armchairs. Moving fewer muscles, with less strength. Strength diminishing with diminished movement. Limberness diminishing with diminished movement. Ideas, feelings, playfulness diminishing with diminished expression. We become quiet, polite, unexpressive.

The years themselves do not diminish anybody. It is the way we have learned to live them, giving up a little of ourselves at each step—whether to survive on a job, please a spouse, or keep peace in the family; whether from exhaustion or pure laziness.

Yet perhaps the state of the physical body is not the only sign of health. What about the Hindu saint Ramana Maharshi, or Suzuki Roshi, a Zen Buddhist teacher and great leader? Both of these spiritual teachers died of cancer. Yet, as they pointed out, the cancer was unimportant to them. It was not overwhelming. They did not spend their days immersed in pain; it was a mere speck on their consciousness. Perhaps health is a way of seeing or experiencing things. Perhaps a highly developed consciousness allows one person to endure physical problems that would overwhelm most people, but without being crippled or submerged. If such freedom of consciousness were a key to health, we wanted to find it and share it with older people.

# CHAPTER 1

# A DIFFERENT VIEW
# OF LONGEVITY

Our culture idolizes the young and creates a dread of age. Hardly anyone likes to think about growing old. This is ironic since the alternative is to die young. Is old age necessarily so terrible? Look at what life is like for older people in other cultures. If you were an elderly Yaghan, living most primitively in the fierce country of Tierra del Fuego, you could expect to be lovingly cared for by your children and never left alone. If you were an Arandan, hunting in the Australian forests, you would be most respected when you became a ''gray-head,'' and you would become gifted with magical powers when you reached your most decrepit stage. As an Eskimo, on the other hand, you might be put out to die in the snow. Each culture deals differently with age.

In ancient China, and in parts of Asia today, an old and infirm member of the family is exempted from worldly duties and freed to speculate on the mysteries of the universe, taking on the role of philosopher. In many cultures, supposedly more primitive than our own, it is the aged, the gray head, the ancient, who presides and explores awareness of being in a spiritual sense, an experience that is sometimes mystical. It is precisely that kind of experience Western young people have sought through drugs and esoteric disciplines. If the older people of our own culture had a tradition of self-development, and devoted their time and attention to spiritual exploration, they would become the teachers of myriad high school and college students and people who now experiment with religions of other cultures.

It seems odd that old age should be so generally unrewarding in a society as wealthy as ours. Many groups on Earth have had less to offer the elderly than we. Where food is short, older people are cared for in a meager way, sometimes abandoned or even killed. But in most societies the elders take on the role of bridge between the mundane and the supernatural. They are the shamans, healers, medicine men and women, sorcerers, priests and priestesses. The Navajos, for instance, would not train a medicine man until he had raised a family and passed middle age; only then was it known what kind of person he was. Contrast this with our training men and women in their 20s to be doctors. In some societies the duties of the elderly begin around age 80. In the United States 80 is considered beyond the pale. Nonetheless we are very interested in longevity and fuss over anyone who lives beyond 100.

In our country the average male life expectancy is almost 72 years, the female 78½, according to *The United Nations Yearbook of Demography, 1988*. It may surprise you to know that although life expectancy has increased more than 20 years since 1900, this represents a reduction in infant and childhood mortality. For those already 65 life has lengthened by only three years. It is said we could add ten years to the average lifespan if we didn't succumb to cardiovascular and renal disease.

The leading causes of death among older people in the United States are heart disease and stroke, cancer, flu and pneumonia, and accidents. Biologist Ruth Weg has compiled a revealing correlation between the diseases of ''aging'' and how we live:

| 1. Arteriosclerosis<br>Atherosclerosis<br>Coronary disease<br>Cerebral accidents<br>(stroke)<br>Hypertension | High-fat, high-carbohydrate diet; sedentary lifestyle; tension; cigarette smoking. |
|---|---|
| 2. Chronic pulmonary disease | Cigarette smoking; air pollution. |
| 3. Obesity | High-calorie diet; lack of exercise. |
| 4. Osteoporosis | Inadequate calcium and protein intake (probably also lack of exercise and poor diet for lifelong endocrine function). |
| 5. Periodontal disease | Malnutrition and poor tooth care. |
| 6. Senile dementia | Malnutrition and isolation. |
| 7. Sexual dysfunction | Low-level health from above factors; ignorance; society's stereotypic attitudes. |

It is clear that our life expectancy and the quality of our later years are diminished by the kinds of stresses we live with; by a high-calorie, fat-rich diet, by a sedentary lifestyle, environmental pollution, and habits such as smoking. We are the richest nation and the most overfed people in the world, yet we suffer malnutrition from eating poorly processed foods leached of their nutritive value and foods that do not give us the balance of minerals, vitamins, fiber, protein and enzymes we need for health. Additives hasten our decline; the added sugar we consume may soon make the United States the diabetes capital of the world. We, as a nation, encourage competition and high performance; profit matters more than people. This creates a stressful pattern of life that is directly related to our consumption of drugs, coffee, alcohol and cigarettes, and to the chronic diseases that impair our old age and eventually kill us.

We also reduce our life expectancy with planned obsolescence: Just as automobiles are manufactured to be abandoned at a certain age, human beings are expected to retire. There is neither economic role nor cultural imperative to give older people a sense of their importance to generations that follow. It is taken for granted that older people should produce less and consume less. Pablo Picasso defied tradition by creating prodigiously into his 90s (including fathering a child).

None of us can look at this distorted picture without wondering how we can extend our health, and our lives—now! To begin with, it may be helpful to look at some of the factors that seem to go along with a very long and healthy life.

There are several groups of people in the world who live much longer than we do. Among them it is common to see an 80-year-old doing heavy farming. Food is sparse. And while life is vigorous, older people have more privileges and make more decisions about how things are run. Although some scientists have been skeptical about these longevity pockets, others have gone to study them. The findings break some myths about the conditions for a happy, vigorous old age: It is not a soft life that extends life.

Among the 819 people living in 1971 in the village of Vilcamamba at 4,500 feet in the Ecuadorian Andes, nine were over

100. The odds against finding nine people over 100 among 819 in the United States are overwhelming. Another long-lived group are the Hunzas, inhabitants of an arid valley among the towering peaks of the Karakoram Mountains that divide Pakistan from China. The Hunzas live on vegetables they grow from irrigation canal water, and they go foodless part of each winter. Their robust bodies are maintained on what we might well consider a reducing diet, averaging 1,923 calories a day.

Both of the above groups are homogeneous, which might seem to imply that it takes special genes to live so long. However, in a corner of Georgia on the Black Sea is a group of Russians, Jews, Armenians and Turks living together in a region known as Abkhasia. They are not genetically singular, yet Soviet medical teams indicated they live to a very ripe old age with very few of the debilities and limitations we accept for ourselves as older people in the United States.

Here are a few facts about their physical health and way of life from *Abkhasians, the Long Living People of the Caucasus* by Sula Benet. In 1972 a team of Soviet physicians examined 3,000 people over 80 years of age. Of those, 1,260 were in excellent health. Excellent vision was found in 2,370 and excellent hearing in 2,640. There are no comparable figures for the United States, but if there were they would most surely be almost reversed. The overwhelming majority of people over 90 were in fine mental health. By contrast, in the United States arteriosclerosis is responsible for many mental and physical disabilities among much younger individuals—people in their 60s and 70s. In Abkhasia tests of protein and fat metabolism showed almost no arteriosclerotic changes. A 16-year study of 127 Abkhasians over the age of 100 showed their blood pressure remained 110/60 to 140/90. Moreover, the elderly in this Georgian community readily recovered from bone breaks or diseases. In the United States an elderly person recovers very slowly from injury. Indeed, many doctors have a pessimistic view of healing among the elderly: "What do you expect at that age?" The Abkhasians do not consider sickness inevitable at any age.

Of course, the quality of their society and their lives is very different from ours. They have no retirement and consider work vital. The work is largely agricultural and the load decreases somewhere from age 80 to 90. A man might stop going up into the mountains with spring herds and care for farm animals instead. A woman stops working in the fields and does housework—serving food to a family of 40.

They always work at their own pace, evenly, stopping to rest, never pushing, never competing, never having a deadline. They are seldom sedentary: They say it is bad for the health to sit.

Their diet is unchanging throughout life: milk, vegetables, raw fruits, wine and nuts. They have no sugar and almost no meat or fish. Food is never twice cooked or stored. Leftovers are thrown away. Nor is food cooked with spices or salt. For breakfast they eat a fresh, vitamin C-rich salad of onions, radishes and pickled cucumbers.

Eating, like everything else in their lives, is in moderation. And they never eat rapidly, nor do they tell bad news or create tension at a meal.

Their mores are dominated by elaborate kinship rules among the huge families. No emotionalism is permitted. Elders are highly respected and children receive privileges according to the rules, not on parental whim. Children are regulated by community rules, never confused, never spared the details of adult life. Within the peer group competition is useless. The older generation allows children to choose their careers and lives without intrusion, probably reducing resentment of parents as well as sibling rivalry.

Physical activity at high altitudes requires deep breathing, an unclogged heart and circulatory system. These people maintain a healthy sexual interest well into old age. One newly married man of 106, claiming he was only 97, said, "A man's a man until after about 100, you know."

Late marriages are common and many women still menstruate and give birth at age 55. Growing up in this society might not seem like much fun. Privileges arrive only with age, and life is ascetic and spare.

Although we can identify some of the factors that may be important in Abkhasian longevity, we Americans could not duplicate the childhood, social stability, work conditions or physical environment of the Georgians. They don't even have a word for "old" in their vocabulary. Instead they say "long lived." The best we can do is create new lifestyles here and rejuvenate bodies that have aged rapidly out of neglect. What we *can* do is change our diets, use gradual programs of exercise, remove some of our stressful habits and the attitudes that produce anxiety. These things will improve the quality of our lives, as well as extend them.

One thing we might ask ourselves is why we want a long life. In some ways the American at 70 must have experienced more than the Abkhasian at 125 who has lived an unchanging, predictable life. If longevity is reflected in how much we perceive and experience, the average American who has moved around, traveled, or who has vicariously experienced many world events on radio, television and in books and movies may be more like a 400-year-old. An American may lack the deep life satisfaction of a person in a more primitive society, but his or her life range of information would be vastly greater.

Time is, after all, the result of a state of mind. It is not a fixed measure. Anybody who has nearly drowned will tell you that it is possible to compress a lifetime into a few minutes, maybe even a few seconds. It is also possible to expand a few minutes so they seem to fill hours of clock time, as meditators sometimes say.

Most of us would like to be able to experience expanded time, live an hour's worth of time in just a few minutes. This is possible if we do exercises that lead to profound relaxation and focus the mind.

One such exercise follows. Read it through to the end before starting it. You may want to practice getting physically comfortable and going through the stages of the exercise, setting a timer and stretching and moving your body before you actually try the exercise.

## HORIZONS OF CONCENTRATION: EXTENDING TIME

This exercise is exceedingly powerful when done with a group, but it can also be effective done alone. If you have a tape recorder you can record the instructions so as to leave a free interval of three minutes. You can play the taped instructions, or you can memorize them and say them to yourself.

1. Once you are ready to experience hours in a few minutes, start by unplugging the phone or taking it off the hook. Be sure you won't be interrupted by phones, visitors or pets.

2. Note the time as you start. Place your tape recorder and an egg timer or alarm clock within easy reach.

3. It is best to do this exercise lying down. Loosen all clothing and take off your shoes. Remove jewelry, watches, eyeglasses. Be sure you are neither too cold nor too warm.

4. Begin to concentrate on the feeling of the contact points between your body and the floor or other firm surface; it does not have to be hard. Keep your spine straight; if you wish, put your head on a small pillow and place another under your knees. Do not lie with your head thrown back or lifted up.

5. While you're lying there, put all your attention on the back of your head and slowly move the focus down your body—to your shoulders, back, buttocks, arms, fingers, and all the way down to your heels. Feel what kind of an imprint your body makes on the surface on which you are lying.

6. Imagine that you have just been dipped in black ink and are lying on a piece of white paper. What parts of your body make an impression and what parts don't touch at all? The parts that don't touch may be a little tense. See if you can let them relax more.

7. Now bring all your attention to your heels. Feel their weight, how heavy they are, how relaxed. Move the focus to your calves. Feel their weight and relaxation. Now feel your thighs and buttocks; just feel how heavy they are, their weight on the surface on which you are lying. Feel your arms, back, shoulders, neck, and the back of your head in turn. Feel how relaxed and heavy they are.

8. Repeat this twice more, feeling your body relax from your heels up to your head and back down to your heels. Relax but do not fall asleep!

9. When you have done the exercise three times, begin to allow a wave of relaxation to come up your body. At this point you may feel heavy or floating. Imagine that you are floating in very warm air or water. Allow your jaw to relax, letting your mouth fall open; relax your cheeks, eyelids, eyes (your eyes are closed), forehead, the place between your eyebrows—which is the place of serenity. Now allow the wave of warmth and relaxation to move from your heels all the way to the top of your head. With every exhalation allow yourself to relax more. Follow your breathing so that as you inhale you feel the warmth of the relaxation coming up your body, and as you exhale you feel more warmth and even more relaxed. Do not fall asleep, however.

10. Imagine that you are floating on your back in warm, shallow water like a heavy barge, and you float into a lagoon where it is sunny and beautiful. The lagoon is very shallow and the water is warm. If you cannot swim and fear water, float on a magic carpet or lie in the grass in the sun. The sun is shining on you gently. Imagine that you arise and walk into a lovely meadow near the water's edge; a meadow where you can hear the birds singing, the insects humming, and see the distant trees. You can feel the grass around you, the scent of flowers penetrating your senses. The fragrance is blowing in the wind. Pick a lovely spot and lie there very relaxed.

11. Now begin to allow your mind to relax just as you did your body. Each time you have a thought just let it float by gently like a cloud in the sky. If you think to yourself, ''This exercise bores me,'' allow that thought to float by without doing anything about it.

12. Give yourself exactly three minutes of clock time. (If you are alone you may have to open your eyes for a second to turn over

an egg timer or a cooking timer, or to set an alarm clock.) Then sink back into your relaxation. After you have done this, enter your imaginary meadow, your beautiful private place. Begin to explore it. See whether it reminds you of some place you actually visited when you were a child. Examine the details. See where you are.

Your experience may seem to occupy a whole day, or perhaps an hour or two. But the actual exploration should have taken exactly three minutes of clock time.

13. When the time is up, slowly take a deep breath, clench your fists a little, wiggle your toes, and move your body just a little.

14. Take another deep breath and stretch your arms up over your head.

15. Slowly open your eyes and look around the room. Sit up extemely slowly while taking several deep breaths.

16. Does the room look different? How long did that experience seem to last? Sometimes people will not believe they have been exploring only three minutes.

After doing this a vehement white-haired lady said to me, "I simply don't believe you! I know I couldn't have gone through all that in three minutes. An hour maybe. It felt like a week, I had a whole vacation. I feel like I've been on a week's vacation in the mountains. I'm totally rested." Many people have this kind of experience, although a few remain conscious of clock time and say so.

This exercise is just one of the variety of ways of achieving time compression. It can be done with the eyes open, simply by intention and awareness. For example, you could set a clock on the table and allow 45 minutes, saying, "This 45 minutes will have to give me three hours." You may already do this, and you can invent ways that fit your life.

As you begin to experiment with your perception of time, you may also begin to ask yourself questions about value—the meaningfulness of each timespan. How much of the time did you feel alive and good?

Where does your time go? Watch the clock one whole morning. Watch what you do with each four minutes. How much of each four minutes can you remember? You will learn exactly how you are spending this valuable time. What parts of each day do you remember? What parts do you not remember? Where did the forgotten times go? When does time move "fast," and when does it seem "slow"? Which four-minute periods are most meaningful? Once you have noticed which time intervals bring you the greatest satisfaction you may enjoy more of them in your life. As people discuss the issues that most deeply concern them very few focus on longevity, but many have stated their fears of being alone, confused and/or dependent, and have wished for meaning and affection, for a more positive view of their final years.

## CHAPTER 2

# CHANGE YOUR ATTITUDES AND THOUGHTS; CHANGE YOUR LIFE

My education was probably a lot like yours—focused on reading, arithmetic and manipulating the world. It did not teach me how to understand my feelings, communicate with others or change my attitudes.

Formal education is not concerned with health, except in a perfunctory way.

The word "health" comes from the same Indo-European root as "holy" and "whole." There can be no health that is partial, that encompasses only our bodies or feelings or spirit. Moreover there is no way we can avoid being whole, for our slightest thought affects our feelings, our cell chemistry, our musculature—and has a subtle influence on everyone around us. Health is linked to our attitudes—even our attitudes about our own physical health. For instance people over 90 years of age and people who have had open-heart surgery have run the Boston Marathon, a 26-mile race. Yet many healthier and younger individuals consider themselves too sick or weak. It is not the medical label that counts. When Indian holy man Ramana Maharshi was dying of cancer, the disease was only a speck on the horizon of his consciousness; yet most of us are filled with dread, fear of pain and self-pity at the very thought of cancer. We have been taught to expect suffering and the atmosphere of most medical clinics and hospitals encourage helplessness in a sick person and anxiety and negativity in everyone around the sickroom. Our society also encourages us to expect to be passive victims, unwanted and suffering as we grow older. We can experience our lives that way—or we can change our attitudes.

We cannot wipe out poverty, illness and social injustice, but each of us can change from inside. We can learn new and different reactions. Let's take an extreme example: The threat of a terminal illness can become an opportunity instead of just a terrible fate. A retired businessman I know was informed that he would shortly die of cancer. That was in 1975. He went to Dr. O. Carl Simonton, who taught him how to meditate on healing. It meant being very honest with himself, and it was not easy—but my friend did it. In 1977 he looked back with gratitude on his illness. "That was the real beginning of my life. I never really knew who I was until I began meditating. My marriage is better than ever. . . . I am happier." Others who would have considered themselves invalids after a heart attack or heart surgery have taken the challenge and used programs such as the Pritikin low-fat diet and exercise regimen to become healthier than they ever were before.

Health depends on our attitude toward life.

Ultimately optimum health springs from the expanded awareness of spiritual development, which enables us to free ourselves of neuroses, be less attached to the beliefs and attitudes we learned as children, and free ourselves of the mental traps we automatically live with as part of our culture.

If the prospect of changing your attitudes is an unfamiliar solution to the "negative" aspects of life, perhaps an analogy will help. Each of us looks out upon the world through a window of intricate stained glass, our mind. Its patterns and colors are created by our upbringing, our location in the world, language, education, genetic heritage, habits and character. As we go through life we accumulate more overlays of color: opinions based on experiences, feelings, likes and dislikes, ways of doing things. We become very attached to our opinions and experiences—although they are only one set of ideas among billions. The light from "outside" must come through our stained glass, which tends to get thicker and sometimes murky as we accumulate layers. Whatever we offer to the outside world we give out through this façade of stained glass, too. It is our filter. You and I cannot experience reality the same way, because our stained-glass filters are different. You might try to persuade me to see less purple, but talking won't change my vision.

For instance, I was brought up in a family that valued privacy. I learned to shut the bathroom door, never speak about money, and be reticent to express feelings. If you grew up in a more open family you may like to chat while you are in the bathroom and would let me know exactly why you are furious at the janitor. My reality tells me you are being coarse; yours tells you I am cold. We cannot persuade each other to see differently. Both of us experience and act through our filters. At best we may be able to relinquish some of the habits and feelings that keep out the incoming light. As I have grown older I am not embarrassed to leave the bathroom door open, or discuss my finances with friends. I am still learning to express feelings more openly. I use these examples because they are basic. There is no aspect of our lives that we don't see through many filters.

## YOUR STAINED-GLASS WINDOW

The following game may give you a rich and magnificent stained-glass-window design, indicating how you see the world. It will be composed of your own idiosyncrasies. It is very rewarding to do this with other people, even in a small group. First, however, you need to spend some time alone, thinking about your experiences in life and writing notes.

1. Get six sheets of paper.

2. Write the following topic headings, one at the top of each sheet:

> Love and Friendship
> Money
> Work
> Family
> Religion
> Health

3. Fold the papers in half the long way. You now have divided them into two columns. On the left write ''Past''; on the right, ''Present.'' The notes you write in the left column will refer to your childhood, to the feelings and beliefs of the family in which you were raised. In the right column you will write about your present feelings and beliefs.

4. Write the following down the far left of the left column, leaving space between to write a few lines. You can always use more paper if you run over. The headings:

> Likes
> Dislikes
> Fears

Desires and Expectations
Opinions and Beliefs

5. Sit down with the Love and Friendship page, for example, and begin to think about some of your attitudes. One woman said, "In my family a girl had to be lovable, because then she would get married: Love was her only way to get a meal ticket." Another said, "I like to be loved—I want to be loved as I am. I dislike people who control or limit or manipulate me because they say they love me." Under Fears one woman wrote, "I'm afraid of being alone." Under Opinions and Beliefs one member of the group said, "Lend money and lose a friend." As we shared our feelings and exchanged attitudes, we discovered that other people remembered things we had forgotten. "I'm appalled at what I've discovered about myself," said one man. "I want my friends to come to me, to help me, be nice to me, but I don't want to extend myself to them." He blushed. One by one the other participants all admitted they had the same pattern. "I like friends and lovers who don't make demands," said one.

Write down everything you can think of in the present, and whatever you remember about your parents' or guardians' opinions and feelings. Sometimes you will notice that you still have feelings and attitudes learned in childhood.

As we discussed our families' feelings and beliefs many of us realized that our mothers and fathers had opposite ideas. "My mother thought friends got in the way of housework. My father wanted lots of people around, especially if they had prestige." "In my family I learned to beware of Jews and blacks—I don't feel that way today." "My family thought friends take advantage of you. The only safe love was within the family. Today I feel the opposite it true. It's only my family that loves to manipulate me."

As you can see, this could be a way of finding out about your feelings, your attitudes, and those of your friends. I discovered I had spent most of my life believing that if I had the "right" relationship, it would transform me and make my life perfect. I also discovered that I wanted my beloved to read my mind so I never had to say what I wanted. It was amazing to see the secret beliefs that dominated so much of my life.

Write out each sheet at leisure, as fully as you can, for both your present and your past.

6. If you are doing this exercise with a group, or another person, share your writings and see if there is anything you want to add.

7. Look over each statement. Would you tell that to members of your family? Did your parents share their feelings aloud, or were they silent? Would you be embarrassed if a friend knew your feeling or belief? If so mark it with an asterisk for privacy. Would you tell your feeling or belief to others? Evaluate the extent to which every statement is private. At the bottom of each page, write an estimate of the percentage of your writing you would consider private and the percentage of your family attitudes that were private.

8. Count the statements: Judge how many you consider negative and how many you consider positive.

9. Find some crayons, magic-marker pens, colored inks, paints, or tissue paper in various colors.

10. Draw a simple flower design.

11. The inner petals represent your childhood home and the feelings and beliefs you acquired there. The outer petals represent the present. Let warm colors (red, orange, yellow) represent positive statements. Let cold colors, (blue, green, purple) represent negative. You can indicate intensity by strength of the color. Each petal represents one major subject from the sheets you have written.

12. Color in the petals from your written sheets. You may want to add shapes and create new color codes, too. Since this does not begin to cover the multiple dimensions of your life, you may want to add petals and internal shadings. For each aspect of each topic you fill in, ask yourself how much of it is private. Cover the private area with soft gray. All privacy areas should be colored twice—first in a hot or cold color, then with gray over the color.

Take your time with this. You may even want to do it over a period of several weeks. When you feel you have done enough, look at the wonderful colored pattern that emerges. Hold it up to a lamp or a window. Look at the colors. Ask yourself: "What is the most obvious thing I can do to let more light come through?"

## ANOTHER TACK

You may want to disregard these categories altogether and ask yourself about foods you like or don't like. You might look at your clothing: Are you fastidious or sloppy? Do you like to see people kissing? Do you like to be kissed? Were your parents demonstrative? Did you express anger at home? How? Do you allow friends to know about your finances? Do you have strong beliefs about handling money?

Whatever you do, be as detailed as you can and as honest. The aim is self-discovery. It is only an exercise for seeing your perceptions as they color your view of the world.

Perceptions are not forever. All of us change. If we decide that we want to deliberately change, the best way to start is by experiencing more pleasure. That may sound odd or even immoral.

Actually it is the opposite of immoral, since we're more nurturing and generous when we ourselves feel relaxed and nourished. It is easier to give out of a sense of fullness. Many of us have become so confused by a Puritan ethic that we think it is selfish to give ourselves real pleasure. Like many of you I grew up thinking that it took some pain, and certainly effort, to be virtuous. This is a habitual filter on our view. We forget the effortlessness of real loving. Remember how a child turns to you with dazzling affection and quite suddenly turns away to do something else. Children constantly explore things that bring them pleasure.

They are not embarrassed to show deep unabashed pleasure in their bodies, their faces. We adults often feel embarrassed by pleasure and spend precious energy dissembling. Pleasure is still a source of healing, of satisfaction, and a way of expanding. It would fill us like the air we breathe, if most of us weren't taught to avoid it. Bad. Wrong. Sensual and sexual pleasure were discouraged among children. Babies are still punished for sucking their thumbs, fondling their genitals, or happily feeling their bodies. This is a destructive message, implying there's something wrong with their bodies and with feeling good about themselves.

Most people would not endure the sorrows and hardships of life without pleasure, yet the kinds of pleasure permitted vary from one family to another, from one culture to another. In our country we think pleasure comes from things outside ourselves—from movies, television, entertainment, food, other people, sports, possessions. If we feel depressed we can always buy something, or turn on the television. We also think our bodies must be healed by doctors, and we forget that doctors cannot heal, that only nature heals. We think we need to be comforted by someone else, or that we can be massaged only by someone else. Worst of all we think we can only be loved by someone else, and we forget that we cannot be in a position to love someone else unless we first love ourselves. Because we have been taught that pleasure lies outside, we are falsely dependent on externals. We relinquish what is actually our source of inner strength: our independence, self-sufficiency and flexibility.

Many of us covet flexibility as a most desirable attribute of youth, and we would regain a lot of flexibility if we could learn how to give ourselves deep pleasure. The process of becoming our own best companions and most pleasurable comforters is almost magic.

Watch how this happens as you try the following exercise. However, for the exercise to be effective you need to do it wholeheartedly, with all your attention. Set aside plenty of time, an hour or so. Make sure you won't be disturbed. Sit in a comfortable place, loosen your clothing and take off glasses and any constricting jewelry. The reason for this is that anything tight causes slight tension, a distraction from your wholehearted concentration.

## PLEASURE EXERCISE

Lean back very comfortably and take deep breaths until you feel your body relax and your mind relinquish its business.

1. Try to recall the most wonderful love of your life. Re-create it. Visualize how your beloved looked, moved, talked, felt. Recall how tremendously "in love" you were. Recall the moments of bliss, pain, anxiety, and magnificent openness it gave your life. Your feelings came about because of something you saw in another person—but it was *your feeling*. Now feel that love long after the

relationship is over. Open your eyes, look around the room with that feeling. Go and do some ordinary thing—holding that feeling, that tenderness. Look at your own hand with that joy and tenderness.

2. Close your eyes again. Recall your most important love in great detail. Who was that person? What does he or she make you feel today? Where did that love go? Where is that love now? Maybe you think it died, or it was caused by some external force that took you by surprise, ambushed you, held you prisoner for a while, then let you go. But look again. Maybe something was triggered within you, releasing your own blissful feelings, so that you could experience the bliss and love around you that you knew as a baby.

Look for some memory of that feeling within you. It is still there, permeating your body. Then slowly, very slowly, open your eyes and gaze around the room with that same feeling. Retain it as long as you can. Does the room look different to you when you have that feeling?

## KEEPING THE FEELING GOING

If you practice this exercise daily for three weeks, you can begin to maintain this feeling in your everyday life. You can summon it wherever you are, without needing to go through the long relaxation exercise. Notice how you react to other people and how they relate to you when you have this happiness within you. It is not selfish or smug to spend time summoning joy for yourself, because you also spread relaxation and contentment around you. As you feel this positiveness and gaze around, see how the feeling changes your perception.

All of us have been deeply in love and imagined that the joy and luminosity came from some magical outer force or from the other person. Eventually something happened and the love seemed less intense. We looked at the same person with different eyes. The world seemed ordinary again. What changed? Of course the change was within us. Romantic love is so highly regarded in our culture and so confused with mating; we are taught to wait for certain very specific circumstances before we may be totally spontaneous with and open to another human being. We say we fall in love. Usually the other person meets certain unspoken inner demands, treats us the way our grandmother or beloved father used to, makes us feel tall and powerful or protected and secure.

We have very complex inner demands or expectations—and when the world meets them we may feel joy or bliss. If a situation or person fits the complex expectations that control our experience, we feel bliss. Most of the time we close ourselves to bliss because our inner demands are *not* satisfied. When we are disappointed we often grow tense and closed and blame the world for failing us. And when we grow tense we seem to suffer more. Our problems look worse. The only antidote is a feeling of openness and joy.

Practice this pleasure exercise often, inventing variations that suit you. As you become comfortable with the exercise you may begin to notice how you control the filters through which you see the world; you can make it rosy or gray. Don't be discouraged if you don't glow with joy the first few times—most of us feel inwardly embarrassed when we are told to feel pleasure. Don't be discouraged if the results aren't dramatic: It takes many repetitions before you notice the change. At first it may even seem these exercises do not, in any way, help you with your real problems—yet ultimately they will inevitably benefit you.

Everyone accumulates problems, but their effect on your life depends on how you deal with them. If a neighbor plays his radio so loudly that it annoys you, do you tell him it is bothering you? And can you tell him pleasantly, so that he isn't insulted? Or do you sit and brood over the interruption? Do you allow yourself to become angry before you do anything about it? Most of our troubles are solvable. The problem is not usually outside—it is in you, in how you react, in how you deal with the outside.

You may be stressed by long lines at the supermarket. Perhaps you could shop when the lines are short, or to do a meditation while in line. You may hate heavy traffic—but you can try to schedule yourself to avoid it, or sing while driving. You may feel an unfamiliar pain in your stomach; you can worry about it, wondering whether you have cancer or a hernia—or you can make an appointment for a medical examination right away. You may have paid out all your money, expecting a check that arrives late; you can sit and fret—or you can tell your creditors and review your finances so you have more leeway in the future.

As things happen we all have gut feelings. Our bodies express tightness, headache, eyestrain, indigestion, insomnia—unless we allow ourselves to feel precisely whatever comes up. Usually we are most upset by unresolved feelings. If I look around in the present, I see that it is a sunny day, and I am in a quiet plant-filled room and I am wearing a green sweater and working at a beige computer. There are no overtones of any emotion: just greenness and light. But in the back of my mind there are faint images of what troubles me. I feel a pull. Some part of my attention is not here as my fingers move on the keyboard. I can, with a little effort, slice that deviating attention off—and suddenly there is nothing else. I am here. It almost seems that the light level has gone up.

I am aware of the vibrations in my body from typing, the way my spine rests and the way I sit.

It is easier to experience the present when it is pleasant than when it is painful. Before group work at SAGE we often argued about the best way to accomplish our goal of greater health; whether we should create new and pleasurable experiences or analyze problems in a therapeutic manner. We did both. We began to see that people who had a sense of immediate satisfaction were better able to relax their vision of things. We played games, silly games.

One bright autumn afternoon we went around the room, each of us singing a line or two from a song we particularly liked. Shyly one woman confessed that she had always been afraid to sing in a group, yet wanted to. We began to urge and beg her to sing for us. After much coaxing she began in a timid voice, singing a favorite Gilbert and Sullivan song. As she sang, with the encouragement of everyone there, she began to sound stronger. When she finished she was glowing. It may not seem like much to people who easily perform in groups, but those who are shy will understand why she was almost in tears when she finished. ''I never thought I could do that. You young people don't know how hard this is. I've spent 74 years creating an identity, and now you're helping me undo it.''

Everyone agreed that it was hard, but an outworn identity can be a prison. And everyone agreed that the small triumphs were worth an effort. They made life more exciting. The old mold no longer had such a toehold. It didn't matter where we started from so long as we began to allow the possibility of new feelings and attitudes.

Starting was very difficult for some people. ''How can I spend time on my own pleasure when there is such suffering in my family?" "I'm an angry person. If I stopped being angry I'd have to stop being a shop leader." "I believe there are more worthwhile things to do than loll around in imaginary scenes." If someone were to tell me to change I would resist—but nobody was telling anyone to change. We were creating an atmosphere that permitted change. I could see others beginning to sing in front of the group or show tears when they felt them. I also wanted to share in their feelings of triumph, of having overcome an inner barrier, of having changed a personality trait they thought was "permanent."

As schoolchildren we received basic training in self-denial and suffering. At the time when physical growth made us want to move we were taught to sit still in school. We went to the bathroom at the teacher's whim, not the behest of our bodies. We were taught to remain silent, obedient and swallow what authorities had to say rather than learning to think. We were distinctly taught not to hear the feelings we had, or the needs of our bodies, as if we were disembodied little intellects.

Most of us have lived out some variation of our cultural message, a message that is not designed to improve our health or well-being. Here are a few of the premises that act as filters of our perception of reality—colored bits in our stained-glass window.

- Virtue means giving up what we want and making efforts to do what someone else considers virtuous.
- To be unselfish, considerate—a good person—we must subjugate our own needs and concentrate on the needs of others.
- It is important to be nice, to be pleasant, even if it means hiding our real feelings and honest thoughts.

- There are higher things to heed than our bodies. For instance, it is more important to sit still and study than to run around and exercise as our bodies may desire.
- A valuable person is one who produces something—like this book, or money—or who performs, is a good cook or a good carpenter.
- Whatever we produce is more valuable if it involves a lot of effort.
- Something that costs a lot must be better than something that costs little.
- Success is important and we need to sacrifice some emotions and spend less time on friendship and family, spend less time relaxing.
- It is important to go after what we want—to grasp and collect things.
- It is bad to show or admit feelings of sadness, gratitude, fear or vulnerability. Our weakness will be our downfall. If bad feelings occur in our bodies, we should go to a doctor.
- If we are physically sick, people will help us; but if we have unhappy feelings, people will look down on us.
- We are the only ones who have inner doubts, self-condemnations. We are terrible people and we had better keep secret what we are really like.
- It is not our fault: Whatever happens, we are victims. We are victims of our diseases.

Ironically our culture gives us messages to nurture weakness in ourselves, to cultivate illness and misery. We have an elaborate legal system that encourages people to play the victim. Yet we all know that we prefer being around people who are happy, self-reliant and harmonious. Human beings are not innately miserable. We have learned to place more and more filters between ourselves and others. As a result many people do feel worse as they grow older and dare not share their inner selves. This isolates them.

In this moment we are alive. You are reading this page at this moment, somewhere indoors or outdoors. You are in a lighted place. You are sitting, lying or standing. You are breathing as you read. You are a radiant being.

We do not have to hang on to our suffering. We may have been programmed and have programmed ourselves, beginning with our childhood responses to our parents. But we are also more than our program, for we can change it. As we increase our pleasure and sensitivity, we loosen the hold of our old ways of being.

## CHAPTER 3

# RELAX AND ENJOY OPTIMUM HEALTH

To be well is not simply to get by from day to day without painful symptoms. It is also a state of consciousness, of joy in living, of vitality—a sense of integration of body, mind and spirit, a sense of integration with people and the world. We know, for instance, that nutrition and proper weight are important. We know that we must exercise our bodies or lose limberness and vitality. We also know that we need love and close communication with others. We need ways of reducing stress and of reacting differently to stress. One of the greatest sources of stress is a lack of appreciation of ourselves, so we need to love ourselves to become healthy. Each of us knows that deep within lies a core that is dimensionless, deep, eternal and creative—an essence we can touch if we are quiet and relaxed enough.

The ability to relax at will is basic to optimum health. If you can master this skill you can move from the crowded basement of events and thoughts to a spacious high floor from which you can observe your life and have time to respond sensitively, with choice. If you can relax you will more easily obtain the other dimensions of health as well. But what is relaxation?

Most of us were brought up to think of relaxation as a state of collapse. Some think it is sleep, oblivion, not being conscious.

Others think of it as flacidity, a total limpness of the body. Some people describe themselves as most relaxed during the pleasant exhaustion after a good game of tennis or other vigorous physical activity. Others feel relaxed after drinking, when in a state of torpor. Many people relax by watching television or reading a good murder mystery. Many are relaxed after orgasm. Rarely do people say they are relaxed while carrying out their day-to-day activities, for the usual image of relaxation is one of a supine body, a sunbather at the beach, or someone sprawled out on a carpet or bed.

Almost everyone would agree that relaxation means the absence of muscular tension. We look at the softness, the flexibility of babies or housecats and see continued relaxation. Pick up a cat and his or her body is soft and pliable, conforming to your arms. Babies, too, seem to be relaxed, although alert, and subject to tension only in brief bursts of anger, pain, hunger, or before trying a new movement. The infant and, presumably, the cat are relaxed throughout most of their day. They are not in a state of collapse. Far from it. Both are exploratory, interested, curious.

Another visible attribute of both babies and cats is essential to relaxation: Neither holds back its feelings. When a baby is upset, the crying is loud and clear. When a cat feels threatened by your gesture, you may get scratched in a flash. Anger, fear, hunger, discomfort, loneliness, merriment and ecstasy are all expressed without censorship. A young child or a cat wanting to be touched is suddenly on your lap. A burst of affection and the child's arms are around your neck or the cat rubs against you and purrs. By the same token negative feelings—sullenness, rage and sorrow—are shamelessly open.

This, too, is relaxation. Much of the tension we feel comes from the gradually learned withholding of emotional expression. Emotional openness is relaxed. Emotional censure requires that we hold back tears and anger, that we tense our jaws, keep our chests compressed, never show fear, and hold our clenched hands motionless when they would beat something in rage.

Relaxation has many aspects. It is not just a matter of tensing and relaxing muscles.

It is a matter of relaxing the whole body.

It is also a matter of relaxing emotions.

Beyond that, it is not possible to relax fully with an unquiet mind. Your mind affects body chemistry, musculature, glands—your every cell. If you sit down to relax but are conducting a long conversation in your head, your mind cannot be quiet; somewhere it is continuing tension in your body.

If you don't believe that your mind can instantly produce such physical changes, try the following exercise. Read it through and then do it:

Close you eyes and imagine a nice ripe lemon. Pick it up and feel the oiliness of the skin. Now take a knife and cut it in half. See how juicy it is. Imagine a glass. Squeeze a few drops into the glass. Now bring the glass to your lips and taste it.

What happens in your mouth?

## THE POWER OF THE MIND

Well, that was just a thought; 90 percent of the people who think of a lemon immediately notice they have more saliva in their mouths, that their mouths pucker a little. A mere thought causes the saliva glands to secrete more. This is the power of the mind to affect the body. Whether we are conscious or not, every thought we have affects our bodies. To relax this incessant mental barrage on the body, we need to know how to quiet our minds so we are not thinking unnecessarily. Relaxation is a state in which we are mentally quiescent, not busily chattering to ourselves. To attain this state people use a variety of exercises, many of them known as meditation. Meditation exercises reduce the internal jabbering and allow us to focus upon a single thought—such as a mantra.

There is still another dimension to relaxation that is extremely important. It may surprise you, but to relax fully and release feelings and thoughts, you need to feel trust in the universe! If you can't trust the universe, you will always want to control it. We cannot relax if we are worrying about whether it will rain tomorrow, or whether we are aging too fast, or when we will die, or how rapidly we can recover from an operation. If we are trying to run the universe we will never be able to relax.

If we need to control everything, including other people, we are unconsciously distrustful of the universe. We don't trust a higher power to have created each person uniquely for his or her own purpose and nature. We need not believe in God to have faith in the universe: It is a kind of certitude that needs no church, no images. It is a certain knowledge in the ''rightness'' of things as they are, even though we may not understand them. At certain times we may feel as Job did, that there are many injustices; but we are limited human beings and cannot judge the whole, since we cannot even see it. Without accepting the rightness of the universe, we must try to control our own fates—we can never relax.

The deep, unarticulated beliefs that lie beneath our behavior and our feelings are the foundations of both tension and relaxation. As we relax, our lives and our bodies change, we have more peace of mind and more pleasure in living.

## HOW RELAXED ARE YOU?

How relaxed are you? The following questions will allow you to observe your own patterns and take stock of your tensions.

1. What are your three most important beliefs?
2. What are your three immediate goals—and what obstacles do you face in achieving them?
3. Are you happy? What evidence would you give another person of your happiness?
4. Do you hurry? When the phone rings, or the doorbell sounds, do you rush? Do you find yourself mentally pressured when you have an appointment?
5. How do you feel about loud noises?
6. Listen to the sound of your breath, or feel the movements—is your breathing slow and deep, or shallow and rapid?
7. How flexible is your body? Can you move your head and neck so that you can see behind you? Can you bend over? Do you feel limber?
8. Do you express your feelings? When you feel sad do you allow yourself to cry? When you are angry can you say so openly?
9. Can you assert yourself, stand up for your rights? Or do you let people walk all over you? If, for instance, a doctor treats you in an insensitive way, do you say so, or do you hold back politely and smolder?
10. Are there situations in your life that repeatedly stress you? What have you done to remove yourself or change them?
11. Do you have a space of your own where you can be alone when you want to?
12. Can you sit quietly and listen to music, or look at an object without thinking of a hundred other things?

13. Can you fall asleep easily?

14. Do you know what things raise your spirits and what depresses you? Do you know what things give you energy and what drains you?

15. Do you become irritable easily?

16. Do you take time out to become absorbed in something you enjoy—a hobby, craft, art, walking in the country, bird-watching, gardening?

17. Do you get some physical exercise each day or every other day?

18. Do you have chronic symptoms of any kind?

If you can answer the first three questions, you are on the way. As a tension index this is crude, but you can get some idea about yourself. If you honestly answer question 4 "no," you probably do not hurry yourself unnecessarily. Question 5: Noise produces stress, and the body responds by shooting out adrenalin and tensing muscles—which return to normal more slowly as we grow older. Try to live in a quiet place. Question 6 is your own index; if your breathing is very shallow it is probably a sign of prolonged tension, and perhaps lack of exercise.

If you are flexible (question 7), and you express your feelings openly (question 8), you are apt to be relaxed. Expressing feelings includes asserting yourself (question 9). You needn't be impolite, you simply need to be honest and to voice your needs.

Question 10 is not easy for most of us; sometimes we have chosen a life situation that is most difficult. It may even be killing us, but we won't give it up. It might be a job with a boss who treats us badly, or a marriage to someone who won't respect our needs. Often we feel we would be judged morally wrong if we made the choice to put our own needs and health first. Of course other people do the judging—remember they don't have to live in your skin. Only *you* can judge what is best for you.

If you can answer "yes" to questions 11 through 14, that is a sign you know how to relax. Irritability (question 15) is usually a response to stress, and a tense person is far more irritable than a relaxed one. The more things get to you and irritate you, the stronger the chance that your tension level is high. Your tension level will diminish with pleasant pursuits (question 16) and daily exercise (question 17).

As for question 18, most chronic symptoms are the residue of prolonged tension in response to stress. If they are severe you have a gauge on the extent to which you have reacted to stress and lived with tension in body, mind, feeling and spirit.

## THE SOURCES OF STRESS

Tension begins when we are in school. Sitting still for many hours a day is not the best thing for children, but that is the first lesson they learn. In crowded public schools children must learn to control their bladders and evacuation until a teacher permits them to use the toilet. That degree of control is also a stress. Children are taught to hide their feelings. That is a stress. After years of controlling feelings it may seem as if they have died. As we learn to deaden ourselves, to not cry, to not laugh too much, to not express feelings the people around us don't want to hear, we also learn to use the logical, language-oriented side of our brain to control and contract our natural selves. We gain something, because we become socially acceptable. But we lose something—our own feelings—and we create diseases.

Symptoms are the body's way of telling us there is too much

stress. Each of us has particular target organs that immediately respond to stress. It might be the stomach and gas, or the heart and angina, or clogged arteries. It might take the form of asthma, or hiccups, or skin irritations, or blurred vision. Many common symptoms may be due to stress: headache, blurred vision, dizziness, fatigue, coughing, wheezing, backache, muscle spasm, itching, palpitations, sweating, rapid heart rate, impotence, pelvic pain, stomach ache, diarrhea, frequent urination, dermatitis, hyperventilation, irregular heart rhythm, high blood pressure, delayed menstruation, vaginal discharge. (Those symptoms might also indicate dangerous illness—check with your physician.)

The foregoing list comes from *Feeling Fine* by Dr. Arthur Ulene, who says they are the most common stress reactions of his own patients. Do you have any of these complaints? Simply recognizing them and paying attention may be the start of changing them.

It is becoming clear to medical doctors that the "diseases of old age" in our country are only indirectly related to age. They represent repeated stress reactions to chronic tension. Of course the longer tension has continued the more likely it is there will be severe symptoms.

It is important to realize that it is our reaction to stress that accumulates and becomes disease: It is not the stress itself.

We actually need some stress and challenge in life, and our bodies contain the natural mechanisms for dealing with it. If somebody says, "I'm going to hit you!" you get ready. Your muscles brace, you breathe a little faster; you are ready to fight or run. Suppose you are really frightened: Your hands and feet get cold as the blood vessels contract and blood goes into the core of your body. Your adrenal glands have put out hormones that release energy from all your cells. With the activation of your sympathetic nervous system your blood pressure goes up, your heart rate increases, you breathe faster, and your muscles have a quicker flow of nourishing blood. Your chemistry is changed. Your gut reacts and gets ready to evacuate.

A brilliant physiologist, Dr. Hans Selye, studied this response to stress and called it a general adaptation syndrome. He saw there are three stages. The first is an alarm reaction; the entire body is mobilized. After this comes a resistance stage, in which the mobilization of the body has raised your resistance and energy way above its normal levels. If the stress isn't over quickly but continues for some time, this heightened resistance will be followed by a period of exhaustion. In other words there is only so much energy to use for adapting to stress. After a while your energy is depleted.

Our bodies seem to have been designed to meet brief challenges. They are designed to discharge a huge energy that is mobilized—to permit us to slay the dragon, to run from the tiger, to put out the fire, to make love, to flee. What happens to that energy when we do none of the above? Our tissues are still in a state of alarm. Our blood pressure still rises.

Actually our bodies go through the same changes whenever we are challenged, but we may not notice because we have been taught to hold back anger, fright and sorrow. We may be driving and someone honks at us suddenly; we are startled but cannot do anything about it. We even feel that surge of adrenalin, which is part of what we call being startled. Or perhaps somebody does something that makes us angry—but we have learned to hide anger, so we don't say anything. We are very polite, but our body is building up the fast pulse and high blood pressure anyway. It lasts a long time. Later we feel fatigued and downcast. We have to take a driving test and are afraid we may fail. There is no way to cry and talk about our fear: We simply tense our chest, stiffen our jaw, and go through the test in a state of nervousness and distraction, upset by our own withheld feelings. Afterward we are very tired.

Think of the amount of difficulty we cause ourselves before an ordeal such as surgery! I remember having no opportunity to tell my doctor I was angry at him for failing to diagnose my polyp earlier—not to speak out and cry about the fear of not surviving. There were many feelings: Each that was not discharged was associated with a tension of the muscles. Muscle tension invariably changes our chemistry. So I actually went into surgery in the worst possible way, without experiencing, perhaps even recognizing, my feelings and instead using my precious energy to suppress them. Is that a predicament familiar in your life and in the lives of your friends?

In childhood I found it frustrating, even enraging, to stifle my feelings; by adulthood I sometimes did not even have the feelings. The cost in energy of such suppression is enormous.

You can demonstrate how much energy it takes to hold back feelings with the simple exercise that follows.

## STRESS TEST

Hold your hand out in front of you, fist tightly clenched, while you read the next page.

At first you may find it painful to keep your fist clenched, but after a while it will bother you less. Keep it tight as you read on.

We learned this clenching as schoolchildren. After more than half a lifetime we can see the results in the posture and texture of our bodies. Look at someone stooped over as if the weight of the world sat on his or her back and shoulders. Look at someone whose shoulders are pulled in, chest flattened with tears and frustrations that were never expressed. Look at people with set jaws, at people who push out their chests and chins defiantly. Look at people who stand and walk with chest collapsed, stomach forward, exaggeratedly curved back.

There is no reason why our bodies shouldn't be as straight in later life as in early childhood.

But children adopt the characteristic postures of their parents, and in too many cases that means the *lordosis* (curved spine), the jutting chin, the pinched-in shoulders. That posture expresses an attitude. It also feels ''right'' to the person because it is the only posture he or she has known. Over the years, if our habits remain the same, the posture becomes ingrained and our bodies are shaped more and more rigidly.

Undoing the tension of a lifetime, at any age, is a slow, patient procedure. Relaxation is not collapse, not being ''spaced out.'' It is more like the relaxed walk of an alert cat. Because you are not merely physical, your relaxation is not merely physical. Even so, you may want to begin by relaxing muscles and focusing on your body.

The tension in your body comes from holding back emotions, not from expressing anger or fear, not from asserting yourself when you have needs. It comes from your mind, always busy thinking, trying to find something, making lists, remembering, planning. It comes from some deeper anxiety, perhaps, that makes you think you need to control everything in your life—the weather, other people, and the way your body reacts.

Now: How is your fist? Did you keep it clenched tightly? Release it. Relax your hand. Do you feel some warmth in your hand? Did you feel some fatigue from maintaining your fist? Or did you cheat and let your fist relax early? If you kept it tightly clenched you will now sense how much energy it drained. This is energy we usually waste. We spend this precious energy holding our bodies unconsciously tense. We don't realize that we are tired from tensing our bodies. We are accustomed to being taut. It is familiar. We no longer feel it because tense muscles send a cacophony of messages to the brain, like heavy static. Relaxed muscles send fewer nerve messages.

What would you do if you had more energy?

Most of us do not associate relaxation with increased energy, yet you can tell from the above exercise that relaxation releases the energy used in tension. This may explain certain extraordinary people who seem to need very little sleep, yet who work prodigiously. I know a psychiatrist who runs a large practice and a research laboratory and thoroughly enjoys all the hubbub of his 24-hour day. He has time to read, meet with friends and travel because he sleeps only about three hours a day. Another man, a Western spiritual teacher, sleeps about two hours a night and eats very little, yet he has as much energy and vitality at 65 as a youngster. Among people who practice meditation and who are satisfied and pleased with their daily lives, you will find many who sleep less and need less rest than they used to. However, you will also find that these people pace themselves. They do not hurry. They rest when they are tired. They spend their energy carefully and only on things that matter to them!

## RELAXATION FUNDAMENTALS

Before you start a relaxation exercise always unplug the phone or take it off the hook and arrange not to be interrupted, even by pets. Make sure your room is a comfortable temperature. If it is chilly, put on a sweater or cover yourself with a light blanket. Loosen your clothing. Take off your watch, other jewelry and glasses; you may not realize these are distracting, yet your nervous system will react to any stimulation—including a constricting watchband.

Allow yourself ample time for each of the following exercises, which should be done sitting or lying down. The great advantage of sitting is that you will not fall asleep. The aim is to *stay awake, not to fall asleep*!

After the exercises take time to feel any changes that have occurred. Don't just get up and resume your activities. You need several minutes for reentry.

## RELAXATION EXERCISES

1. Lean back in your chair and sigh deeply. Feel your feet on the floor and your back against the chair, your buttocks on the seat. Feel the pull of gravity. Each time you breathe, pay attention to the exhalation—and with each let yourself sink more deeply into the chair. Allow yourself to feel relaxed and heavy. Let your arms and legs become heavier and more relaxed. Do this for 10 minutes but do not go to sleep.

When we first tried this in groups, one woman said it frightened her.

"Can you describe what frightened you?"

"I felt as if my body were melting. I couldn't find the boundaries. After a while I felt huge, like a balloon. I thought something terrible was happening to my stomach and feet, but when I raised my head they looked normal."

Odd as it may sound, such unfamiliar feelings are a positive sign of relaxation. Another person in the group said, "I don't like this relaxation at all. I feel as if I'm falling. I have to catch myself. Then I tense up."

His sensation of falling was a common one. He was truly letting his tension go. It did not mean he was having a stroke, as he worried. He was really relaxing his body and mind.

If you have unusual feelings you can be pretty certain they are of relaxation. The reason they are strange is that you are rarely so relaxed while awake.

2. Sitting comfortably, begin to imagine that every time you inhale you are bringing a cloud of warm air through your body. As you exhale, particularly draw the warm air down through your arms and hands. You might imagine the summer sun on your body, or sitting in a warm bath. Now concentrate on your hands. Feel them becoming warmer and warmer.

"I had the most ridiculous sensation when I did that."

"What was it?"

"I felt as if my whole body was getting huge, and it filled up with a delectable orange color. I even started to smell something like oranges. Is it possible to smell images?"

"Yes."

"Well, I smelled oranges and other kinds of fruit. Then I smelled a soap my mother must have used when I was a baby. It was a scent that made me feel very secure and warm inside."

Some people had memories of touch or color. Most began to enjoy it. "I like the sense of power. I can heat my body. I've been a chilly person all my life and now I know I can sit down and all I have to do is think about taking a warm shower and I'm warm all over."

Some people found it easy. Others said it was very hard for them. Some had deep childhood memories; others saw colors, smelled odors, or said it was quite mundane. "I just imagined I plugged myself into the wall like a heater and I lit up," said one.

3. Concentrate your attention on your hands. After taking a few deep breaths to settle down, begin exhaling warmth down your arms into your hands. See how much you can feel your palms, your fingers, the backs of your hands. See if you begin to feel a little prickling. If so, pay attention until the prickling grows stronger and spreads throughout your hands. (You may want to focus on only one hand; pick the one in which you feel the most sensation.) See if you feel some swelling. Let your hands swell up as large as they can. See if you feel some pulsing or throbbing. Allow that feeling to become very strong. Now see if your hands are warmer. Allow them to become very warm.

Warming the hands has been used to help people thwart the symptoms of migraine headache. One woman was truly ecstatic the first time she warmed her hands, relaxed, and felt her incipient migraine attack dissolving.

"I feel really hopeful for the first time in 15 years," she said. "I've had these symptoms almost every day. Now I really believe there is something I can do about them without taking a lot of drugs."

Another woman said, "I feel almost tremulous about this because I have had such trouble with my hands. I have been troubled with terrible pain in the cold, and it doesn't even have to be very chilly out—about 50 degrees. But when I went out yesterday I forgot my gloves and wondered if I should go back and get them. Then I thought, well, I'll make my hands prickle instead. It worked. I was so tickled I wanted to tell all my friends."

"Warming the hands," said one man, "is so relaxing I can go to sleep."

There is always a range of reactions. For every person who loves an exercise, there is one, maybe two, who hate it. Moreover, an exercise will change each time you do it. Don't judge the effects until you have practiced the exercise at least four times. Many relaxation exercises build on one another. As you become more deeply relaxed you will notice different sensations.

And as you practice you will feel the effects more rapidly. As one man said, "It used to take me 15 minutes, and I mean it was a struggle to feel any difference in my hand temperature. Now I can warm them up in 10 seconds. The best thing about it is that the concentration, or whatever, makes me drop all my worries. When I do, my arthritis doesn't hurt me so much."

4. Sit down and make yourself very comfortable. Begin as you did in the first exercise, by feeling yourself get heavier and more relaxed each time you exhale. When your arms and legs feel heavy and relaxed, allow them to feel warm. You can exhale, feeling still

more warmth in your hands and feet, and say to yourself, "I feel relaxed and calm."

5. Now you are going to go on a journey to a special place of your own. Imagine that it is your favorite time of year, and you are in a spot you especially love and remember. Take some time to let the scene come to you—wildflowers blowing on a hill in the mountains, trees in a garden fragrant with flowers—the rolling mists of early morning at a lagoon, or the pounding surf at the shore. As you begin to see the scene you love, enter it and walk around. It is your place. It is a place of quiet and peace and pleasure where no one will disturb you. Spend some time enjoying this place and examining details.

When you are ready to leave, tighten your hands into fists, stretch and take a deep breath. Open your eyes slowly. Take a minute to see how you feel before you get up.

After doing this exercise one woman sat in her chair looking astounded. She was silent for several minutes. "I didn't know I could do that!" she finally said. "I could swear I was in Zurich on vacation—everything was so clear. I can't believe I just imagined that. I feel as if I'd been gone a month."

In many ways the process of relaxing may seem undramatic and slow. It is. Simple things are important. You can allow your stomach to extend and take deep breaths instead of holding it in with tight clothing. You can take time to notice your surroundings. You can take space for your own needs and begin to assert yourself, if that isn't already your habit. It is very important to be straightforward about your needs.

In the beginning all this may feel unfamiliar. For most of us the familiar state is tension, and the early stages of relaxing are the most difficult. But you need to set aside 20 minutes a day for it. You need to begin to know what you are feeling deep inside. Feelings are our natural survival apparatus. They are essential to our well-being—even though we may not always feel happy. Feeling unhappy is part of life; now, however, it is time to give yourself permission to be human—to express feeling and not be ashamed.

Make a pledge to yourself—for the revitalization of your life—to give yourself permission to feel without judging yourself. You will not be ashamed of your emotions. They are true. They are what you feel. They are your guide in life. They are the inner voices that tell you what you need to do—for yourself. Feelings are a gift nature provided for our survival.

At first it may seem your feelings are often negative. As you begin to watch yourself relaxing, as you begin to express yourself from moment to moment, you will begin to discover that they change. They are not always negative. They shift. Chinese medical theory says the suppression of any emotion is the cause of disease and that no emotion takes precedence over another. As you watch your feelings change you may find they are not so important, that none of them last forever. You may even find that you can change them.

## THE THERAPY OF TEARS

Because crying and sadness are so strictly disciplined in childhood—especially for men—they are important expressions to begin cultivating. Crying is an important release for the nervous system, like the steam valve of a kettle. Ideally each of us should cry for a few minutes every day to release tensions that otherwise accumulate in the brain. Far from being ashamed of it, we should do exercises to evoke crying if tears won't come naturally.

At the start, however, be patient with yourself. Treat yourself as a lovable small child. When you feel like crying allow the tears to flow, remembering they are a release mechanism. By holding back tears you prevent your nervous system from getting rid of tensions, so they accumulate. Anyone who has fought tears knows how tension mounts. Holding back when you want to cry involves holding your breath, tightening your neck and jaw muscles, compressing your chest. The next time you feel like crying—but don't dare—feel your body. Feel what you must do to hold on.

As one woman of 74 commented, "We've been schooled to view crying as something to avoid. In my particular case I couldn't shed a tear in front of my husband, and I've been living with him for 54 years."

Not to be able to cry is to be deprived of an important factor in total relaxation—one both men and women need. The following exercise had helped people learn to cry in private.

## CRYING EXERCISE

Make certain you will not be interrupted. Sit comfortably.

Now place your hand over your collarbone. Begin to breathe only as deeply as your hand. Breathe rapidly and make a sound. Listen to the feeling in your voice as you pant and begin to make the sound of a baby crying. Listen to it. Allow yourself to feel its sadness. Allow yourself to make the sounds that go with grief. As you do this, give yourself permission to be human. You should have no trouble releasing. Stay with the exercise if it is difficult at first. Do this especially if you feel the beginning of a headache in your temples, which is often a sign that you have been controlling crying and have accumulated tension and eye pain. Any time you feel a little tension at the temples, take time out and do your crying exercise. When you can work up enough self-pity to sob for a few minutes, you will release that tension. You will feel, as others have, "What a relief!" That relief is relaxation.

We tried crying in a group. One woman said later, "I was unaware of how much I had stored up for so long. I think I cry more because I try so hard to hold it back." She went home and practiced. Two weeks later, she said, "I can cry all right. Now I'm so good at it I haven't been able to read lately because my eyes are swollen from crying. I thought I would feel better immediately, but I feel tired." It took her about five weeks of frequent crying and feeling hopeless and weary before she began to realize what a load she had left behind.

Most people react differently. Some people may cry a little and find it easier to cry when they feel sad or hurt, thereby resolving the feelings at the moment they occur. Still any process may take some patience. We have practiced daily since childhood to achieve tension and self-control! We cannot undo it all in an hour. It is safer and healthier to go through this slowly, not to try to change in an hour or two of exercises.

As you read this, are you aware of how you are sitting? How does your spine feel? Are you aware of the different parts of your body? Can you feel the air around your skin? Can you feel your buttocks on the chair, your feet on the floor? Can you sense your heart beating? Is there a taste in your mouth? What is the color of the light on the page?

Our bodies are vehicles for great pleasure, yet we are taught to restrict our awareness and mainly notice our bodies when we feel discomfort. Sometimes noticing makes us anxious because we have learned to associate almost any unfamiliar sensation with a symptom of illness. Do not be surprised if you have this reaction as you begin to pay attention.

Some people become anxious when they begin relaxing deeply. Relaxation allows you to feel much more, especially in parts of the body that have been tense. As you relax, you may begin to feel energy moving in your fingers and legs, bubbling in your stomach after eating, pulsating in your hands. Feeling a lot means sensitivity, not sickness. At first you may also feel symptoms more. However if you will remain calm and listen to your sensations, you will be rewarded by discovering that there is a rich seething of life going on under your skin.

You will begin to smell, see and hear more acutely. Just realize that it may not be easy to feel again once you are out of the habit. You will not be the first person to feel anxiety when you first hear your heart beating loudly, or sense a tingling up your arms and legs or around your face. Usually people are waking up—not sick—when they feel these subtle sensations. All of us need to learn to feel again, and it takes as much determination as learning to swim or ride a bicycle.

# CHAPTER 4

# BREATHING LIFE INTO YOUR LIFE

One day a lanky retired actor scanned the sunny room and remarked, "I noticed that my baby grandson breathes with his whole body. His diaphragm moves. But when I look around the room, I see that we are just breathing in the chest."

"I get dizzy if I breathe deeply," responded one woman.

"I never noticed how I breathe," commented another.

Anyone who has been sedentary for 20 or 30 years will not breathe very deeply. If you suddenly start taking deep breaths you could start to feel dizzy. This doesn't mean it's bad for you. It means your brain mechanism has to adjust the balance of oxygen and carbon dioxide. The balance depends on how much air you breathe. If you breathe shallowly, on the whole, you have to breathe more rapidly. When you start breathing deeply again, this mechanism takes a little time to readjust. That is why you get dizzy. As you practice, however, your brain resets its regulator: Now you begin to breathe deeply and less often. Soon, deeper breathing becomes involuntary.

If you did nothing but practice some breathing exercises and become aware of your breathing you would radically change your life. People doubt that, and many resist the exercises with vehemence. One elegant woman in her early 70s complained about her fatigue and lack of spirit and energy. ''I hate these breathing exercises,'' she would say, yet by spring she was bragging about her energy and the long, long hikes she was taking. Another woman, venturesome and worldly, was equally skeptical about breathing exercises she was doing at home each day. ''I can't see that this is doing anything for me,'' she said. ''It's so boring.'' But six months later she was telling the group, ''You know, I'm not sure what has happened to me. I used to have trouble just dragging myself out of bed. Now I have so much energy that my body moves faster than my head.

''I got up the other day and found myself in San Francisco—almost before I decided to go. I was up and out. I never really believed that breathing would do this for me. Actually I've been trying to give up smoking. When I feel a yen for a cigarette, I take a couple of deep breaths and the need goes away. I do the same when I'm tempted to snack. I breathe until the hunger just vanishes. Then I do fast breathing if I have difficulty getting fully awake. If I can't seem to fall asleep, I take about 15 to 30 breaths and it puts me right to sleep.''

What is the magic of the human body that makes it possible to obtain both energy and rest from one breathing exercise?

Every time you inhale, a miracle begins. First the membranes of your nose filter the air and kill harmful bacteria while warming the air to body temperature. The cleansed, warmed air goes down your trachea (the windpipe), which divides into two branches, the bronchi, which in turn have extensions—tubular structures called bronchioles. These lead into millions and millions of tiny air sacs that compose the lungs. The lungs, heart, blood and muscles work together to bring oxygen to every part and every cell of the body.

The most important muscle is the diaphragm. It resembles an elastic sheet between the chest and abdomen. When it expands downward, it makes room for the lungs to elongate. The chest expands, the belly expands, and air rushes in. When the diaphragm muscle relaxes the chest contracts, compressing the lungs, and the air is expelled. This rhythm brings oxygenated air into the tiny sacs of the lungs where there is impure blood. A form of energy exchange occurs as the blood takes up oxygen in its red cells and releases carbon dioxide and other wastes, which are then exhaled. The hemoglobin molecule in blood is similar in many ways to the chlorophyll molecule in plants. Chlorophyll absorbs energy from light and carbon dioxide and oxygen are released; hemoglobin absorbs oxygen. Both of them form the link between the solar system and life.

The blood that leaves the lungs is rich and red. It is carried to the left auricle of the heart where a contraction forces it into the left ventricle. There the contraction (or beat) forces it through the arteries into capillaries throughout the body. The blood relinquishes its nourishment by a form of energy exchange. Now the used-up blood returns in the veins. It is bluish in color and full of wastes. The impure blood enters the right auricle of the heart. When this chamber becomes full the heart muscle contracts, forcing the blood into the right ventricle which sends it into the millions of hairlike blood vessels of the lungs. There it is cleansed and filled with oxygen and the process starts all over again.

The heart pumps some 700 gallons of blood each day. How hard it works and how much oxygen reaches our body tissues and brain depends upon how we breathe. The brain responds to the amount of carbon dioxide in the blood to adjust the rate of breathing.

How we breathe affects our heart and our feelings. Many of us breathe only with the middle and upper portions of our lungs. Thus we are ineffective at squeezing out the toxic wastes. The base of the lungs, however, may remain stagnant. When people feel they cannot inhale deeply, they often don't exhale fully. They try to add fresh air without removing the stagnant air from the bottom portion of their lungs. The result is the fast, shallow breathing usually associated with feelings of anxiety, or discomfort.

Long, slow, deep exhalations allow the stagnant air to be removed and fresh air to enter. When breathing becomes deeper and slower, the heart does not have to beat so fast. The heart rate may drop from 72 beats per minute to 50 or 40. The heart is no longer having to work so hard. During a breathing exercise, as the breathing becomes slower and deeper the blood pressure drops, the body relaxes, and the nervous system becomes calm. Deep breathing thus takes a burden off the heart and nervous system.

Oxygen is the essence of life for our tissues. Without a continuous supply of fresh oxygen, tissues age and degenerate. Digestion is hindered. Elimination becomes difficult. The brain requires three times as much oxygen as any other organ. Without it our thinking process becomes slower. We "space out." We tire and cannot remember things. This makes us anxious and tense. Without oxygen, brain cells quickly die.

Shallow breathing cannot give you an optimum sense of being alive, calm and happy or of well-being because it burdens your heart and deprives your brain. Deeper, slower breathing brings about a miracle of change in the body and a change in feeling.

## BREATHING RHYTHM EXERCISE

Probably all your life you have taken your breath for granted. You probably don't even listen to how your breathing sounds unless it disturbs you. You may have learned special breathing exercises for yoga or underwater swimming, but how is your ordinary, normal breathing?

Begin by getting comfortably seated in a chair. Make sure you are wearing nothing that binds or constricts your body. Sit as straight as you can. Now just close your eyes and breathe. Decide which part of the breath you like best: Is it inhalation or exhalation? How do you feel in the moment just after you have inhaled, just before you exhale? How do you feel when you have exhaled all the breath and haven't yet inhaled? Spend 10 minutes just watching and listening to how you normally breathe.

Ask one or more friends to do this exercise with you. Compare experiences. You will discover that people have many different feelings about the parts of the breathing rhythm.

I personally love exhalation. It makes me feel like a child—free and relaxed, swinging up into space. But the pause before I inhale again may worry me if it lasts too long. Then comes the rush of air into my lungs. Instead of relaxing me, though, being filled with air makes me feel stuffed and the slight pause before exhaling is a pause I tend to rush. I can't wait to exhale and relax again.

I am always amazed to hear people say that exhalation makes them uncomfortable. Some say they love the feeling of inhaling, or the pause just after inhaling when they feel full and secure.

## OUR BREATHING ROOTS

All of us are different. And these differences speak about our very distinct patterns of feelings. We are probably alike in one way: Most of us have grown up controlling our emotions with breathing. Certainly I own up to stifling feeling such as anger, grief and fear by keeping myself from breathing, holding my breath, swallowing my feelings. I can remember the time when I realized I knew how to stop my feelings: I was eight, seated between my parents at what must have been my first movie, *A Tale of Two Cities*. Toward the end was a scene of a beheading. I was terrified. My father and mother acted as if there were nothing to be scared of. I looked away because I could not bear to see the screen—and I held my breath. I knew then that I had found a way to keep from crying and ''acting like a baby.''

This began a subtle chain of behaviors by which I would stifle my feelings and do what somebody else told me I should do. And I would hold my breath. Little did I know that you can hurt yourself by not breathing enough, but you can do no harm by breathing.

Nonetheless, many people say breathing makes them feel light-headed or peculiar. It is unfamiliar, like deep relaxation. Where do these sensations come from?

To begin with, the moment you breathe deeply more energy flows into your body. Where there is energy flow, there is motion. This energy flow can manifest itself in many ways: as sensations such as tingling, numbness or vibration; as emotions such as sadness, joy or anger; as actual physical actions such as crying, laughing or striking out. So if you are afraid to feel, one of the most effective ways of preventing it is to control your breathing. Each pattern of breathing has an emotional tone. You can become acquainted with the various kinds of breathing by a simple exercise.

1. Sit comfortably. Loosen any tight clothing. Feel your feet firmly planted on the floor. Now put one hand flat on your collarbone, near your throat. Close your eyes and breathe only into that part of the lung cavity; don't breathe into your chest or stomach. Take ten to fifteen breaths.

How does this make you feel? Take a moment or two to register your emotions.

If you feel a little anxious or panicky, remember that the feeling will not last. Sometimes people gasp or feel as if they had been running. Register you own feelings and then go on to the next exploration.

2. Put your hand on your chest. Close your eyes and breathe into your upper chest only. Do not breathe into your diaphram or stomach. This is not a deep breath. You should move only the part of your chest your hand rests on. Take ten to fifteen breaths.

Once again you may find you had to breathe rapidly to get enough air. Some people recognize this as the way they breathe when they are stifling tears or feeling anxious. If you feel anxious or upset, remember it will not last. Register your own feelings. Then go on.

3. Put one hand on your diaphragm, just under your rib cage. Put the other hand on your chest. Now breathe into the diaphragm. Move that hand, but do not move the hand on your chest. If it seems difficult at first, be patient. You knew how to do this when you were very young. Take ten to fifteen breaths. Close your eyes and register your feelings. Many people say this feels "better," that it is more satisfying. What do you think?

4. Now place your hand about three finger-widths below your navel. This time see if you can draw air way down into your lower abdomen so that when you inhale your hand moves up, but your chest and diaphragm do not move. Your chest will only move at the very end of the breath. This means your lungs are extending fully and filling completely with air. Sometimes this is easier to accomplish lying down.

If you try several positions but still find it difficult to breathe into your lower abdomen, you are not alone. Be patient and keep trying. Try to develop five to ten long, slow, abdominal breaths.

Sometimes an image helps. You might imagine that you have nostrils in the middle of your lower back and that you can breathe directly from this "nose" on your back into your stomach. If that doesn't work, you might imagine that you are filling a long balloon inside your stomach: You have to inhale into the bottom to first fill the end of the balloon.

Deep abdominal breathing may be the most important exercise you ever do. When you look back at the different experiences you have had with these patterns of breathing, you can sense which brings in the most air. If you breathe just into your collarbone, you are drawing air only into the uppermost part of your lungs. That is all you get. And that's not much. You have to gasp. The upper lobes are the smallest part of the lungs, yet many people breathe this way. Some people retract the abdomen, raise the shoulders and collarbones, and breathe shallowly. This is very common among people who wear girdles and tight clothing. A great many people with respiratory illnesses have been breathing this way all their lives.

Breathing exercises need to be practiced. If you simply read these exercises and try them once, they will do you little good. Pick one and do it daily for several weeks.

## DEEP ABDOMINAL BREATHING EXERCISE

The following is the most important of the exercises since you cannot go on to the other breathing exercises until you've learned it. This exercise is best done in comfort and leisure. Be sure you will not be interrupted. Unplug the phone. Lie on a firm surface, preferably a carpet, mat or folded blanket on the floor. Try to lie so that your back is straight. You will need to bend your knees and prop pillows under them so your lower back touches the floor. You may need a pillow under your head.

When you have found a comfortable position, place your hand on your lower abdomen—about an inch and a half below the navel. Take long breaths as if you were blowing up a long balloon. Every breath is bringing oxygen to all your cells, and by transformation turning the food you eat into body warmth and the energy to think, feel and move.

Pay attention to the way each breath comes through your nose and down your windpipe. Feel it filling your belly. Feel your lungs stretching and filling. Feel the rise of the incoming breath, then a momentary pause. Feel the ebbing wave of the breath leaving your body. As you exhale, try to make sure you let all the air out. Pay attention to the air leaving your body and moving out beyond your face. Focus on the brief moment when you have exhaled and the breath is out. You may feel a special kind of relaxation just then. Let yourself fall gently into that relaxed feeling. Then start over and watch the breath coming in.

How much you get out of this exercise depends on paying close attention to your breathing. If other thoughts intrude, that's all right. Let them go by. Turn your attention back to your breathing and how it feels.

## MORNING AND EVENING BREATHING EXERCISES

As you lie in bed each morning, draw your knees up and plant your feet on the mattress. Take ten deep breaths into your lower abdomen, paying attention to each breath. As you do this you will begin to become acquainted with your own pattern of breathing deeply.

During the day if you become irritated, angry or frustrated, you can short-circuit these negative feelings and tensions simply by taking eight deep breaths and concentrating on the breaths as you did in your deep abdominal exercise. Nobody can tell you are doing a deep-breathing exercise. They can only see that you are relaxing in a tense situation.

Every afternoon or evening take time to lie down in this same position for a rest. Take ten deep breaths into your lower abdomen. You'll feel rejuvenated.

Soon after we started this breathing exercise, one man came in with the surprised and pleasant expression of one who's received an unexpected kiss. He said he had been doing his ten breaths into the belly exercise before getting out of bed in the morning, during long waits at the pharmacy, the checkout counter, and while waiting for the stop light to turn green.

But he hadn't noticed the change in himself until one morning when he and his wife went to breakfast. They were talking and he wasn't paying attention to what he ordered. Then he noticed that he had been served the wrong thing. "Before, I'd have blown my stack and chewed out the poor son-of-a-gun behind the counter. But I took three deep breaths and laughed. My wife couldn't believe it. She said, 'I don't know what you're doing, but I know you'd better go on doing it.' That was a dramatic indication that the breathing exercises were changing me from an irritable old cuss into a calm, civilized somebody.''

## THE OXYGEN CONNECTION

Ancient Chinese doctors considered breathing an infusion of energy from heaven. So it is. Literally. Each time you inhale you imbibe oxygen that comes from the interaction of the sun—a star—with plants on Earth. Sunlight is essential for the action of green plants, which generate oxygen into the air. So, as you breathe you take oxygen into all your cells, in essence taking direct energy from the planetary systems beyond Earth.

You might see how it feels to have that image in the back of your mind as you practice deep abdominal breathing. You are breathing in air from the universe and breathing back out into space. Some people say this expands their sense of space. Others say it relaxes them and makes them feel deeply connected with those distant points of light that shimmer in the night sky. One lawyer with severe hypertension found himself doing this rather than just watching his breath. "I can go so far out that I forget everything bothering me after a single breath. It's relaxing, maybe because I feel that each breath takes me way out into space for an eternity."

Once you have practiced abdominal breathing and can do it with some ease, you are ready to learn one of the important keys to self-discovery and growth: roll breathing. When I started to write this book, I went to the members of the first two SAGE groups to find out what exercises people still practiced years after the training period was over. All said they still did the roll breathing.

"I'd rather go without dinner than not do my roll breathing," laughed one woman.

"I do roll breaths in the bathtub when I want to relax."

"I do roll breathing to go to sleep," said another. "I try for ten breath cycles, but usually I'm asleep before I'm through. I also do it to reduce pain and when I just want total refreshment—like when I'm tired."

One man thought for a moment. "I do at least ten cycles to relax before I exercise. Then I do exercises gently, not forcing. Sometimes when I'm working around the house, fixing something, I may turn my wrist or ankle, and if I relax myself by breathing, I don't have as much arthritis pain."

These statements are mostly practical. In the long run, however, sleeping better, gaining energy and reducing pain may seem like side effects of a much deeper process. If you do no other exercise in this book consider practicing this one. Learn it carefully and do it daily.

Roll breathing evolved out of gestalt psychology, Reichian therapy and autogenic training. Actually people have been practicing a similar method for several thousand years in yoga. This type of breathing lets us feel emotions and parts of the body that were excluded from consciousness in early childhood. Feeling is the first step in healing.

Because the body stores all experiences, it is possible to re-experience memories and stored feelings as you make contact with your muscles during this exercise. Sometimes people find themselves apprehensive and anxious. Whatever happens, don't fight it. Allow yourself to be apprehensive for a little while. Fighting and suppressing takes energy and will block the energy that is healing.

Similarly, if you feel sad, let yourself weep. If you are scared, you may want to hold your breath after each inhalation to a count of six. Inhale, count to six holding—then exhale. If you are persistent and do not run from you feelings, your anxiety will begin to abate. If you stop the exercise, the anxiety will remain with you and may prevent you from going further. Give yourself permission to express whatever you feel. It might even be silliness, or euphoria.

## ROLL-BREATHING EXERCISE

Once you have decided to do the roll breathing, unplug your phone and make certain you will not be interrupted for at least an hour. It is particularly important to be comfortable; put your jewelry, contact lenses or glasses and shoes aside. Wear loose clothing; a robe or pajamas are excellent.

Lie on a firm surface—a mat, carpet or folded blanket on the floor or, if necessary, on your bed. Your back should be straight. Place a pillow under your head so you are comfortable, and two or even three pillows under your knees. Take time to arrange yourself physically so that the small of your back touches the surface you lie on and you feel very comfortable. The comfort of a long session requires a straight spine. Your head should not be tilted forward or thrown back. Feel your hips lying on the surface. Do not change your breathing. Just observe it at first. Put your hands at your sides if that is comfortable and place the palms up. This is a receptive position. If you're not comfortable that way, however, forget about it.

When you have relaxed and begun to sense the rhythm of your natural breathing, place one hand on your chest and the other hand way down on your lower abdomen, just above the pelvis.

1. Take ten slow breaths into your abdomen, moving only the hand that rests on your belly. If you find that you move the hand on your chest as well, you need to practice breathing into your abdomen some more.

As you develop your breathing, you may want to try breathing in through your nose and out through your mouth. Some people with blocked nasal passages find that it helps to start breathing in through the mouth. If you must do this, you may want to keep a glass of water and throat-moistening lozenges beside you in case your mouth and throat become dry, since it is disruptive to get up in the middle of a breathing session. Often the process of breathing will clear the nasal passages.

2. With one hand resting on your chest and the other on your lower abdomen, take one long breath into the abdomen. When it is full, add air and fill your chest. As you do this you will first lift the hand on your abdomen and then the hand on your chest. It should be a kind of rolling motion, as if the abdomen were a rising wave, followed by a rising wave in your chest.

Practice this until it becomes easy and natural. At first you may be like the rest of us and try expanding your stomach by muscular force. Your stomach will move out, but it will be hard. Similarly if you force your chest out, it too will feel muscular. And the movement will be jerky.

When you get tired, stop.

Practice again, letting the air go way down into your belly, like filling a balloon. Then let the air fill your chest. After you can feel the roll you can let your arms rest comfortably at your sides.

After ten roll breaths (belly and chest), stop. Breathe normally and lie there with your eyes closed. What do you feel happening in your body? It may seem very subtle. Pay attention to it. Whether it is a slight tingling on the bridge of your nose, your hands pulsing, your feet tingling, a slight feeling of chill, whatever—the energy is moving. If you lie still and pay attention to it, you will feel it travel from one place to another.

Practice the rolling breaths so that you feel at ease with them. "It took me every day for three weeks," said one woman. "It wasn't very dramatic at first." She used this method to get rid of lifelong migraine symptoms.

I remember the first three times I did the breathing myself. I was cold and fearful. I covered up with blankets and lay watching my own nameless fear. After a while I warmed up and the fright melted away. The next time I did it, I began to feel tense in my shoulders and neck, and feel sore spots that hadn't been there at first. Those are places where energy is blocked. You can relieve the soreness by giving them a little massage. Then lie back and see what it feels like.

If you feel taut or tense after breathing, massage any spot you can reach. If you cannot reach, use a back scratcher or bath brush. Sometimes the old sore spots will vanish but new ones will take their place.

You might also feel a kind of buzzing sensation or vibration.

That's good. Pay attention to it. Watch it move. You may have muscle twitches, itching, shivering, numbness, cold hands or tightness. These sensations are all the result of new energy you brought to your body by inhaling deeply. Energy produces activity and this may be an experience of physical sensation, sadness, joy, anger or fear. Whatever happens is what your own nervous system needs at that moment. It is a release of blocked energy. Only your nervous system knows what should be released. No one—not your spouse or the world's greatest therapist or teacher—knows your body better than it knows itself. Your nervous system will release tension in its own way according to its own order and needs. Your nervous system is always right! Therefore, be assured that whatever happens is appropriate and good.

Breathing increases energy and therefore feeling. The alternative is to stop feeling. To be anesthetized. Sometimes the feelings during roll-breathing exercises are unfamiliar. You may not understand what is happening to you. Keep repeating to yourself that it is your brain's way of releasing pent-up blocked energy. Anxiety might be a feeling your body needs to release. So even though it is uncomfortable it is a healthy sign. If you become too anxious and uncomfortable, turn over onto your stomach; you will feel more protected.

When we first began roll breathing, we had no idea what to expect. One woman, under considerable stress, had breathed only twenty cycles when she began to sob angrily. "I hate breathing. It makes me feel too sad." Three months later the same woman was saying, "I use this breathing for energy when I'm in a lull. I do about fifteen breaths and then I feel just fine. Sometimes I use it to relax, to put myself to sleep." The amazing differences in reactions were an indication to us that every person experiences a complicated and unique progression of changes.

Now that you are becoming familiar with this way of exploring yourself, you will want to become more systematic and gain more energy. You can lie with your hands at your sides not touching your body. When you inhale into the abdomen, then into the chest, and exhale, you have completed one cycle. Ten of these breaths would make ten cycles.

It is important to build your routine slowly. It will do you no good to do thirty roll breaths, get dizzy and scare yourself with hypervetilation. Begin with a cycle of ten breaths. Then lie still, being aware of your sensations and feelings. Each day work up to more cycles. Eventually you'll be able to do roll breathing for 30 minutes or an hour.

When twenty cycles are easy, alternate. Do ten cycles of deep, quick breaths in a slow, easy fashion. This may take a little effort. Finally do another ten cycles of long slow roll breaths. Now lie with your eyes closed, breathing normally and feeling.

For best effect you should practice every day. ''I practiced daily,'' recalled one man. ''After 14 days nothing had happened. Then, all of a sudden, I found I got energy from the exercise.''

Repeatedly people said that daily practice was important in maintaining the benefits of the process. One woman said, ''I got my migraines under control, the symptoms that used to be there almost daily were rare and mild, so I stopped doing my exercises on a trip to Los Angeles. And the migraines began to come back. I realized it was up to me. I had to do the relaxation and breathing to prevent the symptoms. Every time I stopped and went back to my old habits the symptoms came back.''

It does not seem so demanding to practice for an hour to remove symptoms that have been bothering you for years. Even so, each person seemed to have to go through the same stages: practicing daily for several months, dropping the breathing, finding old tensions and pains returning, then resuming practice.

Working with a friend or relative—taking turns doing the breathing and the guiding—adds depth and a new dimension to the exercise.

## ROLL-BREATHING EXERCISE WITH A PARTNER

Pick a partner you feel at ease with, preferably someone who shares your sense of adventure and exploration. Set aside enough time and space: It will take two hours for both partners to have a session. Make certain you will be free of interruptions. Get comfortable. The person doing the roll breaths should be lying down with pillows under the knees. The guide should also be comfortable, sitting close beside the breather.

1. Sit comfortably or kneel beside your partner. You should be able to place one hand on your partner's chest and the other on his or her abdomen and still remain relaxed and comfortable.

2. Make contact. It helps to synchronize your breathing with your partner's. If you watch and imitate his or her breathing, you will begin to feel as your partner feels. Listen. If the roll breathing comes in jerks, your partner may be trying to control it. If this jerkiness continues, suggest he or she try breathing through the mouth.

Contact is very personal, and some people are afraid of it. Be sensitive to that. You might begin by saying, "I'm going to place my hand on your hand. Is that all right?" Then do it. Put yourself in your partner's place. What would you want? Start with the hand contact. Is your partner's hand cold or warm? Can you feel the rhythm of his or her breathing in the hand? Go very slowly. When you think your partner is ready to feel your hand on his or her arm, say, "I'm going to place my hand on your arm so you will know I'm here as you breathe." Your partner's eyes should remain closed.

3. Listen, and deepen the contact. Ask your partner to take some deep breaths as if filling a balloon. Listen to the breaths, where they catch. Imitate them. Try to get into a rhythm with your partner. When your partner begins to breathe smoothly into the lower abdomen, you can let him or her rest for a minute or so.

Judge whether your partner is ready to feel your hand on his or her abdomen. Say, "I'm going to place my hand on your belly—your lower abdomen. It will help you breathe to feel my hand." Place your hand low on your partner's abdomen—just an inch above the pelvic bone. Now tell him or her to breathe against your hand.

Two things may happen: Your partner may force his or her abdomen against your hand as if there were a lot of muscles contracting. This isn't what you want; ask him or her to slow down, and explain that it doesn't make any difference how big the belly gets. What's important is that the belly be relaxed. This feels very different and when you've done it for a while, you'll know the difference. Next, say, "I'm going to put my other hand on your chest. I want you to breathe against the hand on your abdomen, then against the hand on your chest." Proceed. Be very patient. Don't tell your partner he or she is doing it right or wrong, but be encouraging. After you have been doing this a while it will seem perfectly natural to you; you'll feel more comfortable. The more you practice, the better a guide you will become.

4. Begin to pace your partner. "I'm going to ask you to breathe against my hand on your belly, now against my hand on your chest, now out. And against the belly, and against the chest, and out. . . ." Keep in mind your partner's normal pacing. Watch the rolling, wavelike motion of his or her body and listen to the breathing to be sure it is not forced or tense.

Now guide your partner in ten long, slow rolling breaths. Watch closely for any changes of skin color or signs of tension or fatigue. If you see these, allow your partner to stop and breathe normally. Ask your partner to pay attention to sensation. When he or she is ready, resume the exercise. Never push or force your partner beyond what he or she is willing to do. After ten cycles of roll breaths at a slow pace, ask your partner to take ten short, rapid, deep breaths. Your guidance will make it easier, but never press your own rhythm on your partner. After the ten short breaths, take your partner through ten long cycles again. That is a total of thirty cycles.

5. Be reassuring. After this cycle of thirty breaths ask your partner to breath normally. Say, "Feel your entire body, and when you want to, tell me what you feel. I will just sit here. Are there any spots that feel tense?" Your partner may feel tingling, sore, or emotional. Assure him or her that this is fine; that any feeling that comes up is the right one.

During the next cycle of long breaths you can massage, gently but firmly, any spot that may have felt sore and your partner wants massaged. Sometimes people say they're not feeling anything. They may mean the sensation is subtle, small. They don't count tingling hands. Ask if there isn't some tingling or warmth in the arms, legs or face. Often the breathing energy brings out emotions that have been held down: A person may feel like crying. Reassure your partner that any feeling is important. "Let it happen, and stay with it." Don't avoid your partner's emotion. Your role is to offer reassurance. You are there to listen, not to advise. You are there to offer a handkerchief if needed, to encourage your partner to go on, to hold his or her hand.

Whatever happens is an important part of a healing process. Don't force and don't try to talk away or in any way stop your partner's feelings—even if they are uncomfortable for you.

One woman in her mid 70s complained loudly. "I hate breathing. It makes me cry. I've cried every day for a week."

"How do you feel after you finish crying?"

"Tired."

"And later?"

"Oh later I go out and do my shopping and I have a lot of pep." After several weeks of crying, the breathing made her feel relaxed and energetic.

Do not judge the roll-breathing session or yourself. Try to be as open and reassuring as you can. You play the role of a guide and anchor—someone to hold on to. I prefer to hold a person who is crying, perhaps to cry with him or her. Do only what feels comfortable to you, and throughout the session keep tuned to your partner's breathing rhythm by imitating it yourself.

Sessions with partners are often deep and powerful to a degree that is hard to achieve alone. Surely you cannot predict what will happen. One woman who had just recovered from cancer surgery lay for a long time breathing with a blissful, serene smile on her face, tears streaming down her face. ''I was carried back to childhood,'' she said. ''It was so vivid. I remembered staying with my uncle, my father, and a little dog I used to love. They promised me they would take me hunting. I heard the ringing of church bells, and the quietness of Sunday. It brought tears of joy to my eyes.'' After this experience she often did the roll breathing by herself.

Another woman who was working on breathing by herself felt it was the catharsis of a long period of pain, lifting a huge burden of unexpressed grief. ''I breathed for a while and then I went into the bathroom and looked in the mirror. I was horrified at who was looking back. I thought of all those who had loved me, and I had to laugh at what they had seen and yet loved me nonetheless. Then I went back into the living room and breathed again and began to weep. I wept excessively for two hours. I wept away a score of sorrows. One year I lost six people. My brother died, and it was so heavy it put me in the hospital. Now I can use the breathing any time I want to wipe out pressures and sorrows. I feel as if I am starting a new life.''

One man had an experience that rocked the house with laughter. He was working with a partner and we could hear him begin to laugh from the other room. He arched his back and flung his arms around her. Hollering with laughter, ''Hey, I love you!'' He could feel the energy surging up his spine and spinning out through his limbs, causing him to move jerkily, like a marionette. It was an unforgettable hour. After that he was never quite the same. He was more lively and gregarious, a sexier man. He moved as if he liked his body, and of course everyone else began to respond to his verve and pleasure in himself.

As you work with roll breathing there is no telling what you will find. It is like a gold mine, a hidden treasure of experiences. Being at ease with roll breathing is being at ease with oneself, and with the realities of being human.

## THE EMOTION CONNECTION

Remember, we *are* emotional beings. Emotions are neither good nor bad; they are merely energy in motion. In order to be human you must give yourself permission to feel and to express. Some people become tight, strained and controlling of their feelings. But they fail to realize that to be human is to have emotions. We could have been born snakes, dogs or chickens. We could have been earthworms or fish. But we were born human, and it would be a shame to waste our passage here on Earth by forbidding our own greater nature, by trying to repress, control or avoid who we are. Knowing who we are is the step to who we can become.

If you do no other exercise except roll breathing consistently, it can be a major step toward a new life. As you practice you will find that your lungs and brain adjust to greater amounts of oxygen. You may breathe thirty cycles then wait. Again, you may breathe thirty cycles and wait. As you get better at it, you may need to breathe longer cycles of forty or fifty breaths and take the air in a little faster to perceive the benefit.

During the first months of breathing and relaxation, people usually exclaim with joy about the diminishing aches, pains and other symptoms. A time will come when each person feels so healthy he or she thinks the daily practice is unnecessary. But after stopping for a while, the symptoms always came back. People simply do not erase tension completely after a lifetime. We need to do deliberate relaxation exercises each day. "It's almost miraculous," said one woman. "My lower back is now well. It was so bad from age 65 to 75 I wore a heavy girdle. Now I don't. I haven't had it on for a year."

One woman looked back on her two-and-a-half years of roll breathing. "I don't have a rigid routine anymore: I listen to my feelings, the way my body feels. I know I am responsible for how I feel, that I have the ability to change how I feel. I feel responsible for myself now, and for my body. I am finally autonomous."

If you learn that you can change your own physical feelings, rid yourself of symptoms, change your feelings so that you feel more optimistic about life, and expand your own awareness, you have taken control of a great deal.

If you have time for only one exercise from this entire book, try roll breathing. It will open all kinds of doors for you.

## BREATHING-FOR-SPECIFIC-HEALING EXERCISE

Your breathing is more potent than muscle relaxants and pain killers. Once you have learned to breathe into the abdomen and can use this to relax yourself, you can begin to direct the attention of your breath. It is best to do this lying down, but it can be done sitting, too.

1. Close your eyes. Now pick out a spot just below the navel. Let your body settle and continue to feel that spot. Take a deep

breath and let it out. Now find a relaxed breathing rhythm and breathe into the spot. When you have taken about twenty breaths, imagine that there is a funnel in the top of your head. As you breathe, the air comes down this funnel through your torso and into your belly. When you breathe out, your exhaled breath goes up through your legs, arms and hands, through your torso and chest, and finally out the top of your head.

2. Open your hands and feel the breath flowing into them. Become aware of the sensations in your hands. Are they cold? Warm? Are they prickling? Pulsating? Now imagine breathing into your hands. Imagine that the air you inhale is a beautiful color. With your eyes closed you may see the color permeating your body as you breathe in. Sense that color coming into your hands.

3. Now focus on your body and see if you feel any sore or tight spots. If you have such a spot—and can reach it—place your hand on it. Now just breathe into your belly. Relax and focus your attention on the spot where your hand is. Begin to sense the color and the feeling in your hand. Let a word come into your mind. Breathe directly into the spot that feels sore, even if you cannot reach it with your hand. Breathe the color into it. Do this several times. If your mind wanders, that's all right; just gently bring yourself back. Continue to breathe the color into the spot that feels sore.

Most people are very skeptical about an exercise like this, especially the first time. It takes some practice to become aware of the color and to be able to focus your breath on a sore place.

"I didn't believe in this stuff," said one woman. "I absolutely didn't, but I had such a kink in my neck. I could see this nodule and I couldn't turn my head. So I did what you told me. I wasn't sure I was breathing right. I put my hands up there and they were icy cold. And when you said to think about a word, I thought of 'gone.' And it's gone! That pain was something fierce, and it's gone!''

Another woman said later, ''I see people running to doctors, or reaching for a pill every time they have a pain, and I realize how much I've changed. I used to be that way. And it didn't even help me. Now I breathe.''

# CHAPTER 5

# SELF-IMAGES

It's interesting that so few people expect to have fun as they get older. Visitors often joined my friends and me during our sessions. They were astonished to find ''old'' people who danced, moved with grace, embraced with affection, were limber and, most important, who laughed and laughed. Why do we expect to become decrepit, grouchy and stiff as we age? Why can't we become sensual, graceful and gracious instead?

It can happen with exercise, contact with people, relaxation, movement, and through a change in attitude.

''One afternoon,'' reminisced a happy woman, ''about sixteen of us were stretched out on the floor of a large living room in two rows—eight pairs of bare feet meeting eight other pairs of bare feet. Why? So we could communicate using our feet, of course. Doesn't everybody do that? Well, right in the middle of our exercise the doorbell rang. A delivery man. His eyes swept over the room of wall-to-wall people, mostly gray-haired, feet in the air, pushing, kicking, caressing, tickling. I tell you, the look on his face was something I'll treasure forever: shock, amazement, the temptation to run. We all burst out laughing; a room full of senior citizens with feet in the air, laughing our heads off. The delivery man was clearly appalled and surprised to see such a bunch of nice old people wriggling around on the floor in such an undignified way. When we all looked at him and burst out laughing, he must have been certain he was in a nut house."

I can only imagine what the delivery man was thinking that day, but I do remember that when I was in my 30s I had very stringent expectations of adulthood that included, among other things, dignity and sobriety. I thought it was belittling for adults to go in for nursery-school games, so I held onto my self-consciousness like armor. I'm often surprised at my own attitudes and don't realize I have negative expectations until one pops out.

What do you expect old age to be like? This is what some of my friends said:

"When I arrived at the first meeting and found myself faced with a group of mostly old women with a few old men sprinkled around, I asked myself, 'What am I doing among all these old people? I don't belong here—not yet—not ever.' I almost defected, but returned out of curiosity. Becoming more involved helped me overcome one more prejudice: I realized that old people were essentially people with varied dimensions. . . ."

"Being put in the category of an older person was a very negative experience. I was used to being with younger people and this was difficult."

"There were twenty-three of us—only three men. I hate being around a lot of older women. That's what makes me hate being an old woman."

"When my mother was 75 she told me, 'I never thought of myself as growing old. In fact I never think of myself as old until I look in a mirror.'"

A handsome psychiatrist commented, "I look in the mirror and see frown marks and wrinkles. My hair is gradually turning from gray to white. It isn't as if I dislike what I see. I just wouldn't mind looking in the mirror and finding my reflection the way it was when I was 40. . . .''

"If I look in the mirror and see any signs of age it's very disturbing."

"I hate it. My body and my mind and the work I can do don't match what I see in the mirror."

"I cannot separate my feelings from my resentment at having extra burdens placed upon me: the responsibility of a handicapped husband who is 10 years older than I. . . .''

As we began to share our attitudes about age, we also wondered where our attitudes would show up physically. "Where do you feel these things in your body?"

One woman said she felt age in her shoulders, as if she had been carrying the world there. Another said she felt it was very difficult to breathe and that her respiratory illness represented her age. One person felt it in his diaphragm, another in her stomach. I feel it in my eyes, farsighted and unfocused.

Where do you feel age in your body? Close your eyes and feel the places.

As we talked about our feelings about aging we also discovered how we limited ourselves.

"The other day I was thinking of scrubbing my kitchen floor. But the brainwashing about being older had such a hold on me I didn't. It wasn't that I couldn't scrub it. It was just that I accepted a false limitation. It's like thinking I should retire just because I'm 68. Why, my father didn't retire from practicing dentistry until he was 83.''

''There are places I don't go because I feel they don't want old people around. I don't really know that's so. I just have that in my mind.''

''I'm 68 now, and two years ago I had pretty much given up hoping there would ever be a man in my life again. Then last year I had the most wonderful relationship I have ever had.''

''I've definitely given up on men. I wish I would hope for something to happen—but I don't.''

''I've even stopped hoping I would make new friends. I'm 83. Until I came here I didn't think people liked me or would talk to me because I was older.''

''I don't think I've tried to make friends, really, in the last few years. I always heard people say that it's harder to make new friends when you are older, so I think I stopped trying.''

''I know I don't hope for much with younger people anymore. I know I won't have the energy to keep up.''

''I can outdo most younger people,'' said a woman of 73. ''I used to think I couldn't. But around here I work a longer day and I don't get as tired as they do. They're always complaining.''

## ARE YOUR PREJUDICES TRIPPING YOU UP?

Make a list. Make it as comprehensive as you can. Include the kinds of clothes and foods you buy or don't buy because you think you shouldn't; places you avoid because you feel unwanted or unsafe; situations you could actually handle, but that you avoid on the basis of being too old—such as scrubbing a floor, painting a wall, climbing hills or stairs, starting a new career, enrolling in college or computer school, learning to dance, buying a pet, traveling alone. Think of things you think you can't do. Inspect your reasons; see if they are rationalizations. Perhaps age is not the real limitation. Perhaps you yourself are.

## LIVING-TO-BE-167 EXERCISE

On one of our introspective afternoons one woman said, "I read where the oldest person in the world just died at 167." Imagine that *you* were going to live to be 167.

Try it. You can always refuse the gift of such a long life. But you might accept it provisionally. What would make the next 100 years truly wonderful for you? Remember, if you have another century to live you are quite young now, even if you are 80. And there are people such as the Akbhasians who are said to live to 130 and even into their 150s. For them, 60 is not even middle-aged. Think about it.

After pondering this for a while, people said:

"I suddenly got very relaxed."

"I suddenly felt very young."

"I felt burdened with so much time. I didn't know what I'd do with it."

"God—I'll be in this group for 80 years!"

There are hidden attitudes about aging everywhere. One woman in her early 70s had just been widowed when she first came into our experimental group. After she recovered and felt more spry, all her friends remarked on how young she looked.

"Why is young so good?" she snapped. "Whenever anyone wants to say anything complimentary to me, they say, 'Oh, you look young,' or 'You seem so young.' I wish they would say something else.'' Her indignation revealed her sense of outrage at what has become a national obsession: We accept that to be young is to be wanted, approved, admired, cherished, to be considered beautiful and strong. To be old is none of that.

How many times do we compliment someone by saying he or she looks younger? How often do we remark sadly of someone, ''He has certainly aged!''

Often we equate youth with an appearance that really means health and relaxation. Lack of wrinkles suggest relaxed, unstressed faces with limber movements and good cheer. A combination of factors produces wrinkles, sagging muscles and white hair. Some are genetic: Many Asians and Africans have unlined faces and dark hair into advanced age. Fair-skinned people may accumulate wrinkles from overexposure to the sun. All of us can acquire wrinkles from tension in response to stress, and from poor diet. Some of the visible aspects of age come from sagging muscles due to lack of exercise. A bent-over posture and dragging walk also reflect response to stress. Our muscles reflect disease and unhappiness. Except for some genetic determinants of skin and hair, most of the visible attributes of age are due to ways of living and feeling—not age.

One day we massaged each other's hands. We looked at the hands we were massaging and felt them. Afterwards we talked about what we had discovered. One woman said, ''My partner's hands seemed so young. They weren't discolored or marked, and they felt strong.''

Once again we experienced a hidden attitude: Unmarked, strong hands belong to the young, not the old. Because this belief is so prevalent and insidious, we did another exercise.

## OLD-HAND EXERCISE

Massage the hands of a friend your own age. Afterward look your partner in the eye and let him or her know that you are paying a compliment when you say, "I notice that your hands are old because they are veined (or spotted or whatever)."

That was an exciting exercise. Each of us was a little frightened in the beginning. We were about to say something forbidden, the opposite of what most of us had learned. We were about to say something that was not socially acceptable. Because it seemed a little threatening at the start, the discoveries were particularly important to us.

This is what people said:

"I knew my partner's hands were old because I found somebody very graceful in them, someone bordering on fragile."

"I got the feeling of somebody who had worked a lot and who is very happy about it."

"I felt all that strength and experience."

When asked if they would choose to give up all that strength and experience acquired during life to be young again, everyone answered loudly, "NO!"

Said a woman in her mid 70s, "Because in our culture age does not have any positive connotation, it's only in the last several years I have felt a little more comfortable with it. It helped me to be in a consciousness-raising group for women over 50. We kept supporting each other by saying that it's good to be 50 or older. That took some of the sense of shame out of it. I remember I asked a good friend of mine her brother's age and she responded angrily, 'We don't ask such questions in my family!'"

We all get caught up in some of those feelings because they surround us. They are part of our society. Our most powerful weapon for overcoming them is to bring them out in the open and look at them. This is especially hard when we've learned to feel ashamed and not to talk about such things. It is often easier to talk in the context of a structured exercise.

## FORBIDDEN-REMARKS EXERCISE

Write down ten things you would not say to another person regarding his or her age. For example, 'I think you look older than your age'; 'You dress like an old woman/man'; 'Your memory is failing'; 'You seem rigid.' Ask a friend to do the same thing and share your lists with each other.

Our responses to this sharing were varied. One woman recalled trying on an old blouse her husband especially liked, but the sleeves no longer fit because her arms had grown heavier with age. Her husband's comment implied that her arms should have been the same at 56 as they were in her mid-30s.

A beautiful and elegant member of the group said she had made herself a new pair of slacks, and when she modeled them for her husband, he said, "Your tummy sticks out." She told us, "I got so angry. At my age, without a girdle, my tummy *can* stick out! I found myself furious that he should expect me to look the way I did when I was young!"

"Oh, men! My husband and brother-in-law both came out with the same thing. In their mind's eye they see us as we looked when they first met us, and that's the way we're supposed to stay."

''I know, this country is so youth-oriented that you can't grow old gracefully even if you want to. I looked in the mirror a week or two ago and noticed that my eyelashes are gone. There are only tiny ones left. It gave me a start. Not that it's so important, but my eyes have always been my best feature.''

As the discussion continued we discovered that we were victimizing ourselves and setting a negative example for our children. Some of us were asking the same kinds of questions at 40 as others asked at 60 or 70. Were our skins too wrinkled to be attractive anymore? Were our hands old and veined? Did our tummies stick out too far? Would we still be desirable in another year? Men and women both wondered whether anyone would consider them attractive. Would anyone want to be close to us?

Look what was happening! We were a group of relatively healthy, happy people in a sunny living room, worrying about our wrinkles and our appeal. Then we realized we were struggling for the right to be ourselves. What a ridiculous struggle! How can we be anything *but* ourselves? Still, we spend most of our lives trying to be something else, trying to be younger, prettier, stronger, more agreeable, more reliable, fitting someone else's idea of who we are. Now we were victimizing ourselves and blaming our age.

''I think we have to be very careful not to suffer from self-inflicted wounds. I find young people very delightful, for example. But I don't find them looking down at me. I'll get a smile from a young person sometimes when I know it's because of my gray hair. But I don't misinterpret that. I wouldn't go out of my way to say someone is looking at me as a doddering old fool, because it isn't true.''

One 80-year-old woman said, ''It's important to me that young people are willing to spend time with us. It's a feeling that we're not discarded; that we're contributing to their understanding, that we have some value to them.''

"Yes. I like being with young people and not having them feel I'm just an old lady and don't understand them."

In the course of our discussions many people found their attitudes changing. Working together revealed new images, a more positive picture of aging and its possibilities as we grow older. A psychiatrist remarked that turning inward and sharing our self-observations was improving relationships.

"It's changed my self-image. I have more energy and am more open to things," he added.

"I see humor in situations more: I'm looser."

"As the oldest one here, I'm surprised that the body gets included in everything. It's been difficult for me. I never thought much about my body or my feelings before."

The process of group discussion and sharing can be a process of developing ever-greater directness and frankness. Gradually each group began to reveal all the little attitudes about aging that had been hidden. Without airing and sharing them we might have gone on pretending they didn't exist in our minds, or that hidden attitudes weren't influencing our actions and our lives. Once we began to learn that others shared our worst shames and fears, it took the power out of those negatives. At some point we have all been murderers at heart, panderers, prostitutes, bribers, molesters, gunmen, thieves. We have all entertained many wicked thoughts as well as multitudes of good ones. We are all human. Within each group we simply have to forgive and accept the fact that humans have a negative as well as a positive side to their personalities.

Having lived a long life makes the acceptance and forgiveness possible. We may have hidden our thoughts. We may have repressed our feelings. But they, nonetheless, have tinted our beings.

When a group begins to accept this broad human frailty, it is easier to express feelings and to talk to each other frankly.

As you comb through your own attitudes about aging, look at your roles and postures: shyness, motherliness, gruff okayness. How often do you count yourself out of life situations because of your age? One 73-year-old woman was so shy and reticent that she could never accept a favor. If someone wanted to drive her to a meeting, she found it hard to accept. She gave easily, but could not receive. "There are so many old people who are disliked by younger people because they're so demanding," she said. "I don't want to be like that." In fact, her inability to accept a favor was not really based on age. "I don't think enough of myself," she admitted. "That is, I have self-esteem but some sort of inferiority complex, too. The world is so youth-oriented these days." Age was merely accentuating a problem that had been with her all her life.

Does that apply to you, too? Do you avoid situations because of your age when you have actually been shy about them all your life? Can you receive as well as give?

As you have grown older have you become more as you really always were? Sometimes our perspective is clarified by visualizing who we were. We explored this with the following exercise.

## 'WHO-WERE-YOU?' EXERCISE

1. Make time; an hour when you will not be interrupted. Lie down and get very comfortable. Make sure you have no tight clothing or jewelry on.

2. Tape-record the following narrative, adapting it to yourself. Or ask a friend or relative to read it to you slowly:

"Take a few deep breaths, relaxing as you exhale. Exhale all your worries, concerns, thoughts.

"Now, go back to when you were 50 years old. Who were the people in your life then? If you were working, what kinds of things were you doing? See yourself clearly. See your arms, legs, body and face. Ask yourself: How do I feel about that picture?

"Go back another 15 years to when you were 35. Who were the people you lived with? What was life like for you then? What did you look like? How did you feel? Get a picture of yourself at that age.

"If your pictures go out of focus, pay attention to your breathing. Breathing deeply will keep you centered.

"Now go back to age 25. What was your life like then? What were your daily activities? Who were the important people in your life? How did your life feel to you?

"Go back to high school graduation time. Can you see your school? Teachers? Classmates? What was life like for you then?

"Now see if you can go way back. Can you remember what it was like to be very small—age two, three, four? Can you recall being smaller than your parents? Can you see them as they were when you were a tiny child? What did you feel like at that age? What did it feel like to be small and helpless?''

3. When you have seen and felt these images, begin to take a deep breath and stretch, and as you stretch take all of yourself in, from earliest childhood to the present moment.

When we first did this exercise together one woman laughed until tears came to her eyes. She had been married twice, and both marriages were very difficult. "I was seeing how I used to make myself over to please my husband. Sometimes I've imagined I want to be 20 or 30 again, but when I look at those pictures I realize I wouldn't go through that again for anything."

"I haven't changed. I am aghast how little I've changed. I was a stubborn baby. I'm just that stubborn now."

"I wish I could have told myself how things would go. I might not have been so frightened and so worried all the time."

Many people wished they could have told their young selves something that would have made the process of growing up less harsh, less insecure and frightening. With that suggestion we developed another exercise in which people could give their young selves some solace. It produced a powerful experience.

Once again you may want to ask a friend to read you the narrative, or you can tape-record it and listen.

## CONVERSATION-WITH-YOURSELF-AS-A-CHILD EXERCISE

Make sure you will not be interrupted for an hour. Lie down and make yourself very comfortable.

1. Focus on your breathing. Allow your jaw to relax, your mouth to fall open, and breathe deeply. Close your eyes.

2. Begin a slow, easy breathing pattern. Inhale to a count of four. Hold. Then exhale slowly to a count of eight. Let the breath come in. Do this a number of times. Then listen to the narrative.

"As you exhale, let all your tension leave. Let your concerns and thoughts go out with your breath. As you relax deeply, begin imagining the house you lived in when you were around 12 years old. See yourself walking through the front door. Go inside and walk around. Now open the door and walk outside. There is a path through a garden. Walk down the path and head toward your favorite tree. As you approach the tree, your mature self will see your 12-year-old self approaching. You can see yourself at age 12, and your 12-year-old self can see you as you are now. As your child-self comes toward you, what help can you offer? Is there any advice you can give? What would you have said to your 12-year-old self if you had met him or her on the path? Could you say something that would have made adolescence and youth easier or more pleasurable?

"Speak to your 12-year-old self. (Allow plenty of silent time for this.)

"Slowly say goodbye, and turn around. Walk to the house and go inside. As you enter the house begin to let go of the past, becoming aware of yourself as you are now."

3. Begin to wiggle your toes and fingers. Move your feet and your hands. Move your legs and become aware of your surroundings. Slowly open your eyes in the present.

As we did this on a chilly winter afternoon, we returned from the sounds of our childhood to the sounds of the hotel we were in and the clatter of the nearby restaurant. Most of us had been far away. One woman was sobbing quietly. Another sat up wiping her eyes.

"If only I could have told myself that I was all right—not to be so scared and ashamed, not to think everyone in the world was better than I."

"I was so timid," said one man, "so afraid of being rejected. If I could have seen myself now I wouldn't have believed it. It would have given me the heart to do better."

"I would have said to myself, 'You don't have to be perfect.' In my family we kids had to be perfect. We had to do everything right."

"I was myself when I was nine years old. I had just read a 15th century novel, a romance in which a message was scratched on a glass. So I took my mother's diamond ring and scratched my name on the window thinking she would be pleased. But all she did was rant about how expensive it would be to replace the glass and how it ruined the value of the house. I wanted to say, 'Oh, I'm good all the time; can't I do anything bad?'"

One man described reliving the death of his father.

We all realized that it would have meant a lot to our young selves to have seen ourselves 50 or 60 years later. It would have been reassuring. We also realized that we were still suffering from events that had traumatized us when we were preteenagers. We were not living wholly in the present, for we were gripped by the past, those painful yet dear anchors of our identity. They hurt, and they told us who we were. Why did we go over and over the most painful events? Why did we hold them so tightly? The discussion began to make us ask some questions about our identities, about who we were at that moment.

We then did an age-old exercise many groups have found ful-filling. This exercise requires only a few sheets of paper, a pen or pencil, and time to contemplate.

## 'WHO-AM-I?' EXERCISE

Again, make certain you will not be interrupted.

1. At the top of a sheet of paper write "WHO AM I?" Take as long as you wish to answer. When you have finished, write the question again.

2. Do this ten times. You may need to take several days or even a couple of weeks to answer "WHO AM I?" ten times.

3. When you have answered the questions ten times to your own satisfaction, write the date at the top of each sheet and put your answers away in a drawer or notebook for six months. Then you may want to repeat the exercise.

The question "WHO AM I?" is a simple one at first, but it be-comes more complex as you think about it. By persisting in your question you may begin to realize you are infinite, beyond any-thing you ever imagined.

The answer is a reflection of all your thoughts, hopes, fears, the material image of your history, your family, your reactions to liv-ing, loves and hates, your special ruts and difficulties, and your weaknesses and strengths. Many of these facets of yourself are sub-tle and inward. Some are hard to perceive. But many of your qual-ities, much of who you are, can easily be seen by others.

That person can see not only what you want to show and would like to be, but all those aspects of yourself that you hide. They are written in the expression of your eyes and mouth, in the lines on your face, in the way you carry yourself and walk, in your way of breathing. Your innermost secrets actually show in your posture and bodily ailments.

We do not come fully formed into this world with nothing but genetic tendencies. You may have inherited fine, dry skin and straight brown hair, but you didn't inherit the way you grit your teeth or hunch your shoulders.

The formative childhood years alone do not create us; we also create ourselves. We play an important part in the drama of self-formation. Events, and our reactions to them, slowly become part of our posture, walk, habits, thoughts and structure.

For instance, if you held your breath under tension as a child and continually restricted your breathing so as not to cry or explode, you may find that you became susceptible to bronchitis, colds, pneumonia and respiratory illnesses. You may have controlled your breathing to hold back feelings of grief or anger in adolescence, but chances are you were not aware of this habit as it persisted into early adulthood. Then at 45 or 55 you suddenly discovered that your respiratory volume was not very good. You couldn't inhale and exhale as much air as you should. Moreover you noticed that your shoulders hunched forward as if protecting your chest. You were not born that way. You didn't inherit hunched shoulders—even if your parents had the same posture. You may have copied them. In any event you slowly, imperceptibly developed them.

If you had a hard time expressing anger or grief as a child, it is likely you have had a hard time expressing it as an adult.

That the habit of withholding feeling should show in your body is an example of our wholeness, of the fact that feelings and body are part of the same whole. Ken Dychtwald expressed it well: "It is a manifestation of the unity of the body, mind and spirit. Our feelings and our flesh and our memories and dreams are somehow stuck together, fit together. When I'm working with a person's body, it's clear to me that I'm not just working with a physical structure that has limbs and moves a certain way. I'm working with a body that is the person. The body is the creation of this person, the expression of this person. The body has to be seen as a whole, because that is how it is created."

To some people this is frightening; it means that anything we think or feel is visible. It shows materially in our bodies. Our negative attitudes and habits imbue themselves in our flesh. On the other hand, if we are the creators of our bodies, we can change them. We can change our habits, thoughts and feelings, and as this happens our bodies also change. For instance, suppose we began to move more—walk, bend and become less sedentary. Our breathing would change. Our muscles would develop tone. We would have more endurance and feel more integrated and lively. Our sense of physical well-being would manifest itself visibly, and we would seem more energetic and cheerful as well. Others would respond more positively to us, and we, in turn, would have a better self-image.

Books describing this process are listed in the bibliography.

# CHAPTER 6

# SELF-IMAGE AND MASSAGE

Self-image comes from deep inside us. It is not just a matter of reason, intellect or will. Self-image changes slowly as our feelings begin to change. Perhaps our bodies always remember the basic nourishment we received from our parents when we were infants, being held and touched. These were our earliest communications of love and validity, and we never stop needing them. In other parts of the world adults continue to touch and reassure each other in ways most Americans don't. In many cultures grown men and women may walk with their arms around each other, innocently and fondly. They embrace without embarrassment, stroke each other and show a certain aliveness and contentment in their faces. But the feeling in the United States is often the opposite; as one member of our group said, "I never liked people touching me unless they were members of my family until I came to this group. Now I am less embarrassed—I even enjoy being hugged."

"I hate people putting their hands all over me."

"In my family it just wasn't done. And you didn't touch yourself. That was considered dirty."

Many of us somehow absorbed the message that our bodies were bad and we should neither explore nor enjoy them. This meant we never learned even the most rudimentary ways of massaging away our own aches and pains. We hadn't touched our own bodies enough to have a tactile map of our muscles and bones. This pro-hibition was a key to a negative self-image for many people. As we talked about the possibility of massage, members of the group frankly expressed their feelings:

"I don't want to take off my clothes. My body isn't pretty anymore."

"It's one thing when you are young. But later. . . . Besides, I've had a mastectomy."

"I'm too fat. I've always been overweight."

"My legs are skinny."

As we went around the room everyone felt ashamed. Could we learn to accept wrinkles, sagging skin, scars, fat hips and tummies, gnarled toes? Was it true that older bodies were ugly? What would it be like to see each other without clothes? We all seemed to fear going naked. By age 14 I undressed in a closet at boarding school because I thought it was wrong for my roommates to see my naked body. If other people found as many faults with my body as I did, they would rather not look at it. In a room full of good-looking people, most of us probably think our bodies are not acceptable.

Massage meant people might see your body. It meant being touched.

"I've never been massaged at all. I'm 74 and I never was sick or anything, so nobody ever massaged me."

"Somehow I feel all right about giving massages, but I don't like to have them."

"The only people who ever gave me a massage were men—lovers."

"I always thought of massage as the kind of thing you did be-fore you made love. It seemed too personal, too involved with sex."

"I never liked my body, so I've never undressed in front of any-one, not even my husband—and I'm 76."

"I'm 32 and I feel a lot like you do. I'm self-conscious about my flaws . . . my breasts are too big."

We all had feelings of apprehension, fear—and excitement—as if we were about to break through an important taboo and discover something. As the year progressed, a visiting massage teacher would arrive on Wednesday mornings when no other activities were scheduled. She would set up a table in front of the fireplace. One by one all the members of the first group overcame their objections. At their own pace they came to be massaged and began to enjoy the stretched-out relaxed feeling.

As we started to work on one another we discovered to our astonishment that everyone had a lovely body. Nobody walked around nude in my family home, so I hadn't seen older bodies—ever. I was as surprised as anyone. People with older bodies were not ugly! Many of them had babylike skin. Their bodies felt good. Women who had lost breasts simply had transparent skin, flatness, sometimes a scar; it was not the unimaginable mutilation we expected. The same thing was true of a colostomy. It was all exaggerated in our minds. Moreover, as people relaxed and enjoyed their massage they became lovelier, pinker, and wrinkles vanished. Lines of tension eased away. They began to look really vital and beautiful.

They would get up after a massage refreshed and look at themselves in the mirror with sparkling eyes, pleased. In a subsequent group we began our massage sessions with six tables in a single room. We started out in robes and towels, intending to begin with shoulder massage. Soon the coverings seemed unnecessary. It didn't seem important to hide our bodies from each other. Perhaps we no longer cared how we looked because we felt so differently about ourselves. From then on the group was never the same—it was warmer, more candid, happier.

"I feel we have let down barriers," one woman said. "We trust each other. That lets me be more relaxed."

If you would like to change your self-image, and also ease away aches and pains, start with the appearance and feeling of your own body. Before you begin any physical movement, you need to prepare your mind and feelings. The following exercises should be extremely helpful.

## BODY-DISCOVERY EXERCISE

Set aside a morning or afternoon without interruptions. Unplug the phone. Make sure you are in a warm room. Wear a robe that opens easily, and be certain you have enough light.

1. Stand naked in front of a long mirror. You are a person from outer space. Move your hand. You don't know what it's for. You've never seen a hand move. You may move your arm and head and attempt to see what causes it to move. If you touch the skin it becomes pink. What remarkable thing is happening beneath your skin? What's happening behind your eyes? Where does the moisture come from in your mouth? Examine this strange, miraculous being as if you had never seen one like it in your life.

When you have seen the miracle a creature from outer space would see if it watched you, take a break. Get a piece of blank paper and a pen or pencil.

2. Close your eyes and breathe deeply for a few moments. Take off your robe and look in the mirror. Draw yourself as you see yourself. Don't expect to be Rembrandt. It doesn't matter whether you can draw or not. Just note some of what you see. Do you see big hips and small shoulders? A big stomach and tiny hips? Are the legs thin or heavy? Are they straight or bowed? Is the chest caved in or thrust out? Do you stick your neck out and carry your chin forward? Do you hunch your back? Do you walk leaning back as if retreating?

What does your face show? What do the wrinkles show: merriment, kindliness, laughter, anxiety, worry, tenderness? Wrinkles tell a story of feelings, of muscle movements, tensions and relaxations. What do yours tell you?

Look at your feet: What kind of feet are they? Are they sturdy, and do they carry you well? Are they slender? Are the toes short or long? How is your arch—high or flat?

What do your hands say? Have they worked hard? Are they strong, gentle, fragile, tender, heavy, childlike, delicate?

What does your pelvic area say? Are you sexual or asexual? Are you tilted forward or back? Is this part of your body as well developed as your arms? Your chest?

Look at yourself from the waist up, then from the waist down. Is there a great difference between top and bottom? Is one part heavier or better developed?

3. Look at yourself for 10 minutes, then write notes to yourself about what you saw.

What some group members saw in themselves:
"I saw a lean and hairy old man—shoulders a little small, but

not bad looking. Strong arms. I have done a lot of work with those arms and hands. I looked at myself and realized I'm not such a dismal old guy.''

"I couldn't stop thinking about how I should look. I mean, I don't want that big stomach. My skin is nice.''

"I thought I wasn't going to be able to stand looking at myself in the mirror. I put it off and put if off. I just didn't want to see myself. I don't know where I got the idea I was deformed or something. I looked, and I said to myself, 'That's me.' I was surprised. I didn't look awful. A little too much lard on the thighs. . . .''

When we asked people what mood they felt before they looked in the mirror, some said they had been quite relaxed, others fearful, anxious, or resentful. As you did this exercise, what you saw was reflected in the mirror, but how you saw it depended upon your mood, your thoughts, and your subtle inner feelings. People who look at you see you through their own feelings, prejudices and conditioning. You look at yourself the same way. We all perceive through eyes of judgment or flattery, happiness or anger—distorted lenses often adjusted to negative feelings. We often see through negative feelings because we are generally in a state of some tension. This also changes our bodies. Tension means our muscles are slightly contracted, our bodies pulled in, our faces more lined and taut.

## THE GIFT OF SELF-MASSAGE

You would look different if you were exceedingly relaxed. Try it.

One way to relax before you look in the mirror is to give yourself a massage. First, however, you need to tune your hands.

We are encased in a physical body, but our energies extend way beyond our skin. Most people can feel a layer of warmth—a thermal layer—around the skin. We know that other energies are radiating from our bodies as well. If you put your hand near your radio or television antenna, the sound and picture become stronger. Bioelectric fields surround us on Earth, and we generate fields, too. Some people see these fields in the form of a radiant aura around the body, like a giant translucent eggshell of light. Saints have been pictured with halos, radiant energies around the head. Saint or not, everyone has this kind of radiance or aura. When a person comes close, he or she enters your field. When you move near someone, you enter that person's field. By paying attention to the sensations between the palms of your two hands you can begin to learn how to feel those energy fields.

Begin by tuning your hands.

1. Sit comfortably. Take several deep breaths. Pay attention to how your breath flows. After you have reached a relaxed state, begin to pay attention to the feelings in your hands.

2. Rub you hands together until they are warm and tingling.

3. Move them about two inches apart and hold them parallel. Put all your attention on the palms of your hands and inner surfaces of your fingers.

4. Imagine that the air between your hands is growing thick, maybe even gelatinous.

5. Move your hand slightly—like an accordion: closer, farther apart. You may feel a magnetic pull between them.

6. Pay attention to what you feel. You may feel heat. It may seem that there is a density between your hands. You can stretch it by pulling your hands apart. You may begin to feel prickling, tingling. As you practice you will begin to feel great sensitivity in the inner surfaces of your hands.

7. When your hands begin to feel sensitive, hold your palms over your face and close your eyes. Do your hands feel anything? Does your face feel anything? Try your shoulders, your legs, your chest.

If you do not feel much of anything at first, you are normal. It takes practice. Do this exercise every day. You can do it lying in bed. You will surprise yourself by feeling very acutely with your hands. You will find that you can feel other people without acutally touching them.

Tune your hands this way before you start a massage. Of course you will want to be sure you are not going to be interrupted and that your room is quiet and warm. If possible do your self-massage in a place where you can comfortably leave your upper body nude.

## SELF-MASSAGE: FACE

You will now become both the masseuse and the person being massaged. Treat your body like that of someone you love. Feel the shape of the energy from your face.

1. Close your eyes. Place your forefingers beside the bridge of your nose, one on either side. Make small, firm circles down the sides of your nose. Feel for the place where your cheekbones be-

gin. Firmly press your cheekbones, feeling the structure of your skull. Pressing on the cheekbones near the nose will help you clear your sinuses.

2. Make firm circles along the cheekbones to the jaw muscles. To find your jaw muscles, open and close your mouth. Feel the hinges and firmly, slowly massage those muscles. Let your mouth hang open.

3. Bring your forefingers under your nose and press. Now firmly and slowly begin to massage your gums through your upper lip, working toward the ears. Feel your gums with your fingers. Now switch and feel the fingers with your gums.

When you have massaged your upper gums, do the same to the lower gums. Make slow firm circles, starting in the center and working toward the ears. Massaging the gums will help them stay healthy. People's gums tend to recede as they get older and massage helps them regain tone. Moreover, people with dentures say they fit better when the gums are massaged.

4. Massage gently under the chin and around the cheeks.

5. To massage around the eyes always begin at the bridge of the nose and work toward your temples. Never press your eyelids. Make firm, slow circles with your fingers on the bony orbit around your eyes, starting at the bridge of your nose and working outward. Do the lower orbit, then do the upper orbit. Massage them three times. People say this refreshes their eyes and that they see better afterward.

6. Place your fingers or your palms together in the middle of your forehead and pull your forehead toward your temples as if you were stretching taffy. Do this several times to take the tension out of your forehead.

7. Don't forget your ears. We expect to hear keenly, yet who

among us does anything to help the circulation in our ears? Grab the top of each ear. Use two fingers on each ear, pulling and stretching the rims in a circular motion, moving downward toward the lobes. Pull the ear lobes. Do this three times.

Now place the palms of your hands over your ears. Press and pull your hands away very quickly. This gentle popping will stimulate the inside of your ears.

Take a deep breath. Now look at yourself in the mirror. Your face looks more refreshed, alive and smooth.

## SELF-MASSAGE: NECK

1. Turn your head to the right, then the left. Feel how easily and how far you turn it. This massage will loosen your neck and can help relieve the tension that causes headaches.

2. Take a deep breath and tune your hands.

3. Slide your hand up the back of your neck to the top vertebra. Find the place where your spine and skull connect. Feel the ridge of your skull. Right below the ridge of your skull is an indentation. If you cannot feel it, raise your head and look up at the ceiling, then feel for the hollow. Place two fingers there, or your thumb, whichever is more comfortable. Close your eyes and breathe. Make slow, firm circles.

Do five circles the first time. Work up to ten. As you massage, the indentation will become more relaxed and will feel deeper. Be patient. Do not expect it to happen all at once. With a little massage each day your neck will loosen up considerably.

4. Staying at the base of the skull on either side of the indentation, you will feel muscles. Place two fingers at the top of each.

Again make firm, slow circles. As you relax these two points, you will also relax your whole body.

5. Move along the ridge beside the muscles about two finger widths. Again make firm circles at the base of your skull. These points may feel slightly tender. If you have a headache, massaging these points gently but firmly may help you rid yourself of it.

6. Bring the flats of your hands, or all of your fingers, to the back of your neck. Start at the base of your skull and firmly smooth the big muscles down toward your shoulders. Smooth all the muscles of your neck the same way. If this is an area in which you have aches or soreness, you may want to learn several different strokes.

You can use the flat surface of the hand to slowly, gently stroke muscles. In severe pain you cannot go further than this. It helps the circulation and will soothe pain as the muscles relax. The same slow, long strokes can be done with greater pressure if the muscles are more relaxed, but not if they are in spasm.

After sore or stiff muscles are relaxed, you may feel granules—like grains of sand. These usually hurt. By pressing them with your fingertips in a circular motion, you can disperse them and relieve the trigger points of your pain.

If your problem is circulation you may want to knead a muscle by squeezing then gently releasing it. This is a particularly good stroke for the following massage.

## SELF-MASSAGE: SHOULDERS

1. Sit or stand comfortably. Place one arm behind your back. Run your other hand over your chest to the opposite shoulder.

Squeeze the shoulder muscles. Knead them. Close your eyes and feel your hand kneading your shoulder and neck muscles. Take a deep, long breath. Another.

The reason for holding one arm behind your back is to relax that muscle and make it more amenable to massage. If it hurts, do not do it.

2. Slide your hand back down to your chest. Now place that arm behind your back and massage the other shoulder with your other hand.

This is a massage you can do before you dress or after a shower. If you do it in the spirit of providing love and stimulation and pleasure, you will bring your body alive. We have been taught to be embarrassed at the idea of giving ourselves pleasure. Yet this is what we require to be fully alive.

Try to keep your mind on your massage. Pay attention to your fingers as they move and maximize the benefit of your massage. When you are finished turn your head from side to side. See how your neck feels.

The magic of massage is not mechanical. It requires attention to the feeling of your fingers dancing on your muscles and skin. Paying attention may take some practice, but everything we do well does. Think of the hours a baby practices trying to stand up—and no ballet dancer practices more than a child learning to walk.

If you massage yourself mechanically it will only improve your circulation. If you do it with attention, however, and allow yourself to feel pleasure, something very different will happen. As you practice feeling pleasure, your innermost self-image will begin to improve.

"I do that neck massage every day. I can turn my head more easily to see cars behind me when I'm crossing a street. I don't get so knotted up driving."

"I can remember the first time I gave someone a neck and face massage. It was a woman in my church group. She had a terrible headache. I did the back of her neck, and she said her headache was gone. I don't have headaches myself anymore."

"I don't know why I don't massage my whole body every day. I feel so good afterward."

"After I've done it for myself for a while, then I like to do it for someone else."

We began massaging our own hands, feet, legs, arms, necks, shoulders and faces. Some people signed up for massage courses with good teachers. Others paired up and massaged each other. There are good books of instruction available.

Massage has a sordid connotation for many people. However, the process of examining our attitudes and of developing real bonds within groups allowed us to see that the existence of sleazy massage parlors should not deprive us of this healthy way of relaxing.

One group was feeling so relaxed the members were ready to learn whole-body massage. People brought robes, bathing suits and towels that afternoon. There were three rooms with massage tables. In one room people worked clothed. In another they were nude. In a third they did whatever felt good to them. Nobody *had* to do anything.

People arrived very excited, keyed up. They joked a lot, and acted nervous. One woman in her 70s had never undressed in front of anyone, not even her husband. A man in the group had never seen any woman other than his wife nude. Everyone felt hesitant and anxious. Before the beginning massage the group sat around and discussed their fears. We asked how many people have the opportunity to do something really new in their lives at this age.

"It is really taking a risk. I don't think I'd ever do this on my own. I know I wouldn't."

"How many older people actually have the chance to begin giving and receiving massage?"

"I suppose we all have the chance; we just don't seem to do it."

"Hey, I'm really nervous about this. What is my wife going to think if I go in the room where they undress?"

The experience was unforgettable for everyone. Afterward the group sat looking at each other, and smiling.

"Why didn't we ever discover this before?"

"I know—it's these clothes that keep us apart. I feel so much closer to you all now."

"You know, women look older with their clothes on. When they take them off they have young bodies underneath."

Everyone in the group seemed to agree. They looked better without clothes. They felt better about themselves, knowing that. And feeling better about themselves, they were suddenly much closer. There had been many barriers to closeness in their lives— fears and poor self-images, clothing and convention. After the massage session they discussed how much more comfortable they were with each other and how they had repressed their sexuality.

This feeling of comfort and closeness did not vanish after the session was over. The group had taken a very big risk, had overcome lifelong barriers and made a breakthough. From then on the members began to trust each other deeply about other things in their lives, about illness and relationships. The members had begun to overcome the sense of isolation and coldness they had complained about earlier; they were on their way to developing a real and reliable intimacy.

# CHAPTER 7

# INTIMACY

How many deep, intimate relationships do you have in your life right now? If you can honestly answer that you have one or more, you are most fortunate—and unusual.

Intimacy was almost a taboo word when I was a child. It implied a sexual relationship, but it seemed that even pornography was more acceptable. Sex surely did not create intimacy. Married couples lived together for many years and had sexual relations without truly knowing each other. Intimacy was more threatening than sex, somehow, and more compelling. People were afraid of it. Why?

Perhaps intimate relations, such as we have with our brothers and sisters when we are very young, provide our best opportunity to be honest and open with others because of the unaffected feedback. In an intimate relationship we can reveal to another person the worst of our fantasies, the silliest of our beliefs, the inner recesses of our minds and feelings. Genuine intimacy implies that we lower our defenses, reveal who we really are, and are responded to in kind. Intimate relationships may offer our only hope of learning about ourselves as adults.

How many of us look back on our lives and realize they have lacked intimacy? I am among many who have had a long marriage with almost none. Like others under those circumstances I felt separated, isolated. I longed to be accepted for who I was. By talking about it in a group I managed to overcome some of my barriers, shyness and withdrawal. The group became intimate, and there was a new atmosphere in the room. It did not have the secretive quality of sexual intimacy, but rather a warmth, a satisfaction. Some people said they did feel sexual; others described themselves as childlike, free, secure and playful. As time passed it became clear that all of us longed to live more of our lives in this open state. These were the good times. The exciting times. The times when we could take risks, such as venturing to massage each other.

Close contact was valued, and it was not random. As a group became more secure, more candid and closer, people noticed a shift in their feelings about each other and in their own self-images. They also noticed their family relationships altering. "This is the biggest change in my life," said one woman. "I never used to like being close, except with my grandchildren, and they were small. Now I find it relaxes me. I even asked my husband to give me a shoulder massage the other night. I never would have thought of that before."

Certain well-picked exercises brought about an immense change in self-image. One that is exceedingly simple you might try with a friend if you wish to risk deepening the relationship.

## INTIMACY EXERCISE

1. Close your eyes and take three very deep breaths. Sigh and relax.

2. Sit with your back against your partner's back. This is easier if you are sitting on the floor.

3. Feel your partner's breathing rhythm through your back.

4. Sense your partner's feelings through his or her breathing. You can do this by imitating your partner's breathing.

5. Without speaking, lean on your partner very slowly. Relax and let your head rest against your partner's head. Let your shoulders relax. Lean back on your partner as far as he or she can bear your weight. You may be able to lean on your partner completely, totally relaxed.

6. Your partner should begin to straighten up very slowly, allowing you to continue to lean.

7. Massage each other, back to back. You may massage your partner by rolling your head against his or her neck and shoulders. Now put your hands behind your head and feel your partner's neck.

8. Let your partner lean on you and repeat the procedure.

9. When each of you has leaned against and massaged the other, turn and face each other.

10. Without speaking, decide which of you will first feel the other's face. Gently put your hands on your partner's face, exploring the features. Both partners' eyes should be closed. Then let the second partner explore.

11. When each of you has gently explored the other's face, open your eyes and tell each other how it felt.

A great buzz went through the room after this exercise. Two women who had not known each other well threw their arms around each other. "I didn't know I liked you so much. Then I felt your back rubbing against mine. It was your spine tickling me." People were astounded at the pleasure and relaxation they derived from feeling one another back to back. They were amazed at the affection conveyed in that simple contact. When they explored each others' faces, they touched each other with a caring gentleness they hadn't felt an hour earlier.

This exercise is subtle; each step leads to the next. If you were to reverse the order and touch each others' faces first, neither of you would have had sufficient time to relax and sensitize your body. Without that relaxation you cannot respond openly and tenderly when another person touches your face. Whenever you do an exercise like this one, it is important to move very slowly. Afterward it is good to breathe deeply, to sigh and let yourself feel the full impact of the experience. This exercise leaves people glowing if done at a leisurely pace.

You may think you do not like being touched. One woman in our group confessed that for 83 years she had resisted even casual physical contact with others. "I was never married. I live alone. I just didn't like anyone touching me." But after the group had done some breathing and a contact exercise of this type, she said, "You know, John was stroking my arm and I thought, 'I feel like purring.' I really liked that. My whole body felt as if it were being stroked. I felt so good I decided I liked being touched after all."

There is no secret to how these exercises work. They give you a chance to relax fully, then to establish a wordless contact. A pleasurable physical touching allows you to be open, to be caring and honest at the same time. Intimacy is a state of strong personal two-way communication. Without intimacy we have no way to really see ourselves, no way to grow. Without that human bond there is no escape from our usual thinking patterns.

Psychologist Eugenia Gerrard offered the class an example that is an exaggeration of what happens among older people in our society:

"I was thinking about a man I worked with who didn't want to be touched at all. He had Parkinson's disease and didn't like to lie down for long. He'd start shaking, and that embarrassed him. Over time we worked out physical exercises to help him open his chest and voice-projection exercises to help him get his voice again.

"The really demoralizing effect of the disease was that he lost his positive image of himself. We began to work on this with mirrors so he could look at his face and see what parts were immobile and didn't show much expression. He was really excited by the feedback. He'd reached a point where the muscles around his mouth were totally rigid. He began to realize that this was a self-defense mechanism.

"That was an exciting revelation at age 67. He said, 'God, I began to see that I've been doing this all my life, but now my face is like a mask. It's gotten so heavy.' As soon as he got in touch with this habit he was able to start changing it. I think the important thing about feedback is that until people see what they are doing, they can't change. In working with or relating to someone, you need to give—and receive—honest feedback.

"I'm working with three people who are 80 years old. One woman wanted me to give her a massage, and she began to talk about her body—how it used to be beautiful, but now it was flabby and ugly. This was the beginning of changes for her, because she let me see her body as she talked. She could feel her body, and it still had a lot of vitality and gave her pleasure. But that wasn't the way she described it."

Lack of intimacy, lack of honest response, allows us to become strange, weird, "off-the-wall." Older people in our society do not get much day-to-day honest, nurturing feedback. Suppose your voice was weak and you snapped your fingers to get attention, but people never asked why you were snapping your fingers. You might snap your fingers more insistently, since the gesture was being overlooked, and perhaps clear your throat. It is, after all, extremely frustrating to have something important to say and have nobody listen.

After a while you might overhear a passer-by say, "Oh her, she's dotty. She just sits there making that face and grumbling and snapping her fingers. She's crazy."

But nobody has bothered to find out what is going on.

In small ways we ignore even the people who are closest to us. We don't seem to want to reveal our true selves nor do we ask others about the parts of themselves they keep hidden. This is dangerous in the long run. So long as we hide and maintain barriers between ourselves and others, we are stuck. We hide from ourselves, and we consequently hide from others. This is understandable: Our own fears, insecurities and senses of inadequacy or weakness hold us closed to ourselves and others. But it also puts us in a position of living lives that are not quite real, of having relationships that are not quite satisfying, of feeling neither loved enough nor free enough to be ourselves. All this makes it hard to face both joy and suffering.

If we deny ourselves intimacy we deny ourselves the nurturing and the honest help we might use to open up. Yet *with* intimacy we discover that whatever we have to hide is no worse than what others are hiding, that our friends and neighbors have the same problems, drives, curiosities and negative feelings we have.

One way to help rid ourselves of the sense that we, alone, are living in this hidden and harsh way is to allow the delicate relaxation of exercises to bring us into contact with others. Try exploring another person's face.

## EXPLORING-A-FACE EXERCISE

1.  Find a partner to work with. You can sit on a couch, chairs or the floor, but one of you must be directly behind the other. The person seated behind is the explorer.

2.  Both of you should remove eyeglasses and earrings if you wear them.

3.  Sit quietly and take five deep breaths. Pay attention to each breath. Close your eyes, both of you.

4.  As the explorer, reach around your partner and gently explore his or her face with fingertips and hands. Explore as if you were blind and needed to feel the contours of that face in detail—the hairline, nose, cheeks, jaw, lips and eyes.

5.  When you have felt the contours of your partner's face in detail for about 10 minutes, move back slightly and put your hands on your own face. In what ways does it feel different from the face you were just exploring? Could you recognize your own face in the dark just by feeling it with your fingers?

6.  Switch positions and roles: Go through exactly the same steps taking ample time and not speaking.

7.  Now both of you open your eyes, sit face-to-face and share your feelings. What kinds of things came into your mind as you were being explored? As you explored? What kinds of feelings did you have?

"I never realized your face was so much like mine!" exclaimed a delicate woman in her 70s to a woman in her 30s. "It was so soft, and our mouths are both small—and our bones, too. I felt like your sister. But we don't look alike."

"I never noticed your ears before. I got lost just going around your ears."

"I felt your fingers on my face. Your fingers are so light. It was very loving and I wanted to hug you."

"I could feel how beautiful your face is—but totally different from what I see with my eyes. Isn't that strange? I felt more love touching you than just seeing you."

Needless to say these exercises have been extremely popular even though people often balk at first. Another exercise of this kind allows you to speak to your partner through the palms of your hands.

## LISTENING-HANDS EXERCISE

1. You and a partner sit comfortably facing each other. Place your palms against your partner's palms. Close your eyes and take a deep breath.

2. Listen to your partner through the palms of your hands. You can move your palms, but don't speak. Get to know your partner through his or her palms. Give yourself 10 minutes.

3. Open your eyes slowly, look at your partner and share your experiences.

This seemingly innocuous exercise often drew out people who had never spoken in groups.

"I felt a sort of pulsing energy in my hands," said one woman. She was pink and her eyes looked excited. "My partner let me in. She wasn't frightened at all. I would come in very close. I felt as though I were the aggressor and she didn't enter my space very much. That puzzled me. She and I are very different on the outside, but we feel similar on the inside.''

"It was rather like a dance," said one man, stiffly.

"My partner was willing to explore and be adventuresome. I think he would be an interesting person to do things with."

"I felt I received complete trust, and what I wanted was more stroking and more love."

Perhaps the important aspect of such exercises is that the partners do not talk until after the experience. This allows everyone to experience each other freshly, in a tactile way, and without the usual judgments.

## FOOTSIE EXERCISE

Another variation of the above exercise is done lying down. You can do this without a guide or you can use these instructions as a narrative that can be read to you slowly or played on a tape recorder.

1. Find a partner and pick a place where you can lie with the soles of your feet against each other's. You are going to communicate only with the soles of your feet. This is a good exercise to do with someone you don't know very well. You will discover how much you can learn about another person through the soles of his or her feet.

2. Place your feet against your partner's feet and lie still. Experience the feeling of your partner's feet. Don't do anything else. Feel the pressure of your partner's feet on your own so that there are spots you are more aware of than others.

3. One of you say hello with your feet. Introduce yourselves to each other. Now lie still and just experience your feet again.

4. Let your partner introduce, say hello, and do something your feet might like.

5. Now press your feet against your partner's feet. Be aware of your partner even though only your feet have touched. Be aware of some new information you have about what your partner is like, and what he or she has to share with you.

6. In some way let your feet do something you think your partner's feet would like. In any way that's comfortable you can move both your feet on one of your partner's. You can press, stroke, and share something new. When you have given your partner something, stop.

7. Let your partner give you something and receive it. Spend a few minutes giving and taking whatever you'd like.

8. Now slow down. Be aware of your feet and your partner. This time do to your partner's feet what you would like him or her to do to yours. Slow down and place your feet either side by side or against your partner's feet. Be aware of your partner and the strokes or contact he or she seemed to appreciate.

9. After a few minutes, exchange roles.

10. Now be aware of your feet again and, lying still with your eyes closed, think of the style you use to argue or fight. How do you usually do it—by provoking, pecking, withdrawing, or becoming sullen? With your eyes closed, and using your feet in your own special way, pick a fight with your partner. No sounds, just your feet. Exaggerate the fight. Now slow down and become quieter. Make up with your partner, in your own style, with your feet.

11. Exchange roles so that your partner picks a fight and makes up.

12. Now each of you do to your partner's feet what his or her feet told you they would like.

13. Become totally passive. Take deep breaths. Feel you partner's feet. If you can imagine that the contact with your partner's feet gives you a kind of direct link to his or her feelings, try to get a sense of what it would be like to be him or her. Try to imagine really being the person who is your partner, mingling your perspectives. Allow yourselves to open, to become receptive to your partner. Perhaps you have learned something about his or her uniqueness, sensitivity and needs.

14. Keeping your feet in contact, breathe in slowly and deeply and exhale fully. Take five very deep breaths. And now, with your feet, say goodbye to your partner.

15. Slowly withdraw your feet and lie still for a moment. Feel your feet and how much you have learned through them.

16. Sit up and share your experience.

"I felt embarrassed about the contact, shy or self-conscious," said a younger woman in the group. Her partner said, "Oh, that's too bad. I loved it."

"I thought Mary was very loving. That was the feeling I got from her."

Mary asked, "How do you like the way I fought?"

"To me it was like a little cocker spaniel. It made me smile."

Fighting was an important topic. Most people had never shown irritation or anger in a group. Now they were sharing how they behaved when they were angry.

One couple—a handsome, lanky pair who had been married for 52 years—were particularly pleased with the sharing.

"I didn't fight the way I usually fight," said the wife.

"How would you usually fight?"

"Straight on. I don't stop. I just go straight, pow!"

"How do you think I fought with my partner in this exercise?" her husband asked.

"You gave back what you received," the wife replied.

"No, he didn't do that at all," said the husband's partner. "He just completely withdrew. I couldn't find him at all."

"Well, he doesn't do that usually. He waits until I fight and then he says whatever I've said to him back to me."

To be able to fight, even with the feet, allowed us to say things we had never said to each other before. One woman told her partner and the group how it was to feel his softer side through his feet. He was usually gruff and undemonstrative. "I felt one side—one energy—that was very strong, and one that was lucid, open and receptive."

He said, "She come across in her feet warm, friendly, almost youthful. I felt unequal. It would have been nice to subtract a few years. I envied her a little."

"My personality came out clearly. I was concerned about my feet being so cold they'd be uncomfortable."

"They weren't cold. You were soft and tender, but also quite a definite person. A person who likes fun, who's playful."

A few weeks later the husband and wife who had been married 52 years practiced this exercise at home. They were glowing and excited as they talked about how much it helped their relationship. "We told each other things we had never said before in all these years." It was a new way of listening to each other, of suspending the old habits and being together in a different way. It broke up some kind of logjam, some kind of trap people get caught in whether they live alone and stick with a routine or have been married a long time.

One woman in her mid-70s said, ''Well I am just feeling all kinds of things I haven't felt in 20 years. It's almost shocking.'' She laughed. ''I didn't even know you could just touch somebody's feet and feel so much—so much joy and oneness. It's like making love, really. A year ago I'd have been embarrassed to say that. I didn't know you could have something like orgasm from just touching somebody's feet—or you could be so close!''

## TANTRIC-RITUAL EXERCISE

Asian spiritual disciplines developed what are known as Tantric methods whereby people can combine their energies in a disciplined manner and achieve union on a level that is primarily spiritual rather than sexual. The important first step in any kind of union is the emptying of one's mind.

(If you think this is not pertinent to you, try sitting with your eyes closed for exactly 10 minutes. Notice all your thoughts, images, fantasies and sensations. You may discover that your mind is busier than you thought.)

Tantric yoga is a demanding discipline in which the participants practice concentrating and breathing in order to unite body and soul. Actually, the first step in any kind of tuning in to another person is to breathe in the same rhythm. Sit next to someone and adopt his or her breathing pattern. You will begin to have a glimmering of what the other person feels. Breathing together brings an understanding no words can achieve, and a deep intimacy.

## THE SEXUAL IMPERATIVE

Almost no one had been encouraged in the skills of intimacy because during childhood and youth sexual relationships, whether with the opposite sex or the same sex, were taboo. In one of our groups four of the seven women had attended girls' schools. When they were in high school, dating as it is now was not even imagined.

"My brother took me to dances," recalled one woman with a shy smile. "He chaperoned me wherever I went. I never danced with any other boy. I was lucky to have a brother; that meant I could dance with somebody besides another girl."

Touching, holding hands, talking frankly and even sharing fears about sex were forbidden when most of our group were teenagers. "Nobody in my house would dare mention sex," said one woman, and five others nodded. "I didn't know anything about it; my mother gave me a book. I feel I still don't know very much compared with these younger people. I can't believe it. They seem so free. I wish I were going to school now!" Her words seemed to express what many of the women in the group felt.

"I was very shy," said one man.

This group had been together for a year and a half and, although reluctantly at first, began to broach many topics that had never come up in our discussions before. The members resented feeling that sexual love was only for the young. "I went to a sexuality seminar," said one woman in her early 60s. "It was very important for me. We had to tell a stranger things we had never discussed about sex before. I used words I never used before. And I met someone I had an affair with. It was the best sexual relationship of my life. I wish I had known those things all the years I was married.''

There are a lot of myths about sexual inadequacy and aging, and our society perpetuates the idea that desire is cooled by the years; that frail, older people may be in danger if they make love, that people become sexless as they age. Actually we all know these are myths, but they are part of an entire cultural outlook. Sexuality is more than the reproductive system, hormones and intercourse: It is relationship with a capacity for involvement, intimacy and warmth. It is reaffirmation of the connection between ourselves and another person.

By talking about sexuality openly, with people who are relaxed and feeling close, it is possible to take some veils off the stereotypes. One thing we quickly discovered was that while men may fear impotence as a sign of age, at least older men are encouraged to remain sexually vital.

As one woman said, ''It's fine for a man of 70 to marry a woman 30 years younger. It's even okay for a woman of 20 to marry a man old enough to be her father. But if an older woman goes with a younger man, it's considered awful. Older women are just left out, considered repulsive.''

In our group the women between 65 and 75 outnumbered the men. Some of the members were married. But a marriage of 30 to 50 years often slips into monotony; and sometimes this leads to lack of interest in sex or to involvement with other partners. In one group most of the women thought physiological changes were overrated as the cause of decreased interest in sex.

''I believe these exercises we are doing have reawakened feelings in me that I forgot I could have,'' said one.

The famed Kinsey Survey found that not only did women not lose their capacity to become sexually aroused as they aged, they actually could overcome the effects of hormone depletion and other age-related changes by having an active sex life. Kinsey reported that women who masturbated regularly remained more sexually active and capable of intercourse. Indeed, contemporary gerontologists have found that sexual dysfunction generally results from *other* factors—such things as disease, overeating, alcoholism and emotional disturbance.

Many studies indicate that regular intercourse might be a way to maintain physical tone, since it is like climbing a steep staircase or running: It raises the heart rate, blood pressure and oxygen consumption the same way strenuous exercise does. The increase in some adrenal steroids may create a greater sense of well-being, especially in people with arthritis. Thus, far from being a threat to life, sexual activity may be therapeutic.

Masters and Johnson developed a successful method to help older people with sexual complaints. They suggested having sexual activity early in the day when energy and hormone levels are at their highest. They recommended masturbation to preserve potency in men and glandular lubrication in women, as well as to stimulate general well-being. It is also important to maintain a balanced diet and an exercise program. There is now an abundance of research and clinical evidence to show that sexuality is just as basic in later life as in youth. Because of the enormous change in the past couple of decades, sexual habits, inhibitions and education can be openly shared. This gives access to resources most older (*and* younger) people did not have before. Our society's image of older people as neutered is purely a myth, but by repetition it has been elevated to the status of fact. Many older people have accepted the fiction; unfortunately, many professional therapists, too, have gone along with it.

Actually, the need for nurturing *increases* in later life when there are more losses. Nurturing means many things, and sex is not necessarily one of them. It means touching and affection. It means acceptance and intimacy. If nurturing does lead to physical love, older people may need a new kind of sex education to understand and extend their capacities for relationships and to express the affection and feeling that go with being alive.

As we talked about intimacy, about the need for closeness, for sexual expression, for intense relationships, some people began to consider new lifestyles: polygamy, living in groups rather than alone, relationships with people of the same sex.

By creating taboos against unorthodox lifestyles we have been keeping ourselves apart. In fact, some of the worst problems of age derive not from aging itself but from giving in to society's myths and rules. Looking at those myths and rules, figuring out what you really believe and how that affects your life, becomes a source of new alternatives. It is surprising how new attitudes—and relaxation—can make one feel like a new person.

# CHAPTER 8

# COMMUNICATION—
# GIVE AND TAKE

All my life my mother tried to tell me who she was, but I was 50 before I ever listened. I will never forget sitting on the lawn that sunny afternoon under the giant palms of Esplanade park overlooking the Pacific Ocean. I had brought my mother to this manicured garden directly from the convalescent hospital after her hip surgery. As she took in the sun and spaciousness she was a captive audience. I wanted to practice the new communication skills I had been learning.

I said, "Mom, while we're sitting out here I want to experiment with a communication technique that I think is wonderful. I'm excited about it and I'm telling you this because I want to feel closer to you. And I feel proud of myself in showing off what I've learned."

I then told her that I had just demonstrated the five parts of a clear statement:

The content.
My opinion, or belief.
My feeling.
My intention toward her that prompted me to speak.
The inner motivation or intention toward myself that prompted me to speak.

She replied, "Darling, that's so boring. I want to *talk* to you."

"Please bear with me for just a little," I said. For the next four hours I doggedly used the principles I had learned in class—to both speak and listen to my mother. I listened for the five elements in her speech and when they were missing, I gently inquired about her belief or why she wanted me to know something. My mom was by now talking a blue streak. And I was just as exhilarated. I suddenly understood my frustrations as a child and as a childish adult. I realized that I had spent the past 40 years wanting my mother to act like somebody she was not, and never had been.

I had longed for a nurturing, feminine, cookie-baking mother who loved healing an aching head, fussing over ribbons and trimmings, took pleasure in the soothing prettiness and softness of home. But my mother was actually an artist first and foremost. She had no time or interest in such frippery. As I drew her out I began to hear her excitement as she described her painter's vision. She talked about Van Gogh, Cezanne and Knaths. Her voice became ecstatic as she talked about particular paintings and the use of white. I heard things she had never told me before. That afternoon our friendship deepened and with it our love for each other. Instead of prolonging the expectations of the unsatisfied and angry child, I saw her with awe and appreciation. Why did I have to wait more than 40 years to appreciate the special person my mother was? Why did I have to wait so long to establish the deep bond with her I had always wanted?

Like most of us, I never thought much about communication. I talked without thinking. As emotions came up, I expressed them. It never occurred to me that my endless arguments with my mom, my unsatisfied longings in intimate relationships, my frequent sense of being misunderstood all spoke to one thing: lack of attention and skill. Naturally I never imagined that any of my discomfort and misunderstanding came from the ongoing dialogue in my head that left me too occupied to listen because I was too self-involved to respond with clarity and completeness.

Communication among humans is pretty deplorable. We are so afraid of revealing ourselves, so unskilled at stating the truth that we become estranged even from our own families. Truth—or lack of it—threatens our entire nation. There is no such thing as a flourishing economy without trust. The lack of clear communication is so widespread that most people who need to feel understood seek a counselor or therapist to listen to them. We pay someone to listen instead of developing the skill all people with ears and voices should be using daily.

Twenty years ago a sociologist at a major university demonstrated how to create instantaneous senile dementia in college students. In this experiment over a few days' time, the communications of these college students were ignored and they received no feedback. Whenever the students got irritated at being deliberately discounted or overlooked, or made gestures to demand attention, they were treated as if they were crazy.

Like many ignored people in institutions they began to grow more withdrawn and some began gesticulating in bizarre ways. Pretty soon they were unable to participate and cope in the manner expected of them; they acted like demented people.

They were in the same position as many older people in nursing homes. Many older people get no feedback. Feedback, as opposed to criticism, is the tool by which we learn to socialize. Without it, just about all of us would seem demented. Worse yet, we would feel rejected and quite isolated.

Listening and actively responding sounds very simple. Isn't that what we all try to do in our daily conversations? In truth, it seems, we don't. Active and intentional listening requires some willingness to become unselfishly available to another person. Moreover, skill is needed.

If anything we were taught to hide and obscure our feelings, avoid disclosing our intentions, and deceive the listener into perceiving only our dressed up, presentable selves. When I was growing up I was taught to give a double message; to hide my real reasons for saying things. I took my message from my parents or other adults.

I was taught to be polite. "Don't say you need to go to the bathroom—say you have to close the dog door and excuse yourself." Needless to say, the dog door became an ongoing joke among us kids. Then there was the matter of disclosing feelings. "Dear, you had no business telling Mrs. Greef that you're frightened of her. What on earth could you be frightened of?"

Many of us have learned how to seethe underneath while presenting a calm exterior. I was often confused by people who would shout at me that they were not angry. Even more confusing were the well-intentioned people who wanted to help me. However, instead of listening to me long enough to find out what I needed, they would begin loading me down with their opinions and advice. I would feel guilty. Here was a kindly, generous friend trying to help me, yet inside I was feeling irritated and angry. Instead of gratitude, I couldn't wait to get away. My thank you was a lie.

In the days when we were running SAGE as a sizable organization our decisionmaking committee was run with the help of a communications expert who had worked in large corporations. What Hugh MacLean taught us, we quickly passed on to our groups.

The two most important things our coach taught us:

1. *Speak in the first person:* You may recall all the situations where you were asked to take a stance rather than speak as yourself. In college I recall receiving good lessons in pomposity. I learned never to speak nakedly as "I." There was always some authoritative and cautious way of putting things. For instance: "*It is believed* that Shakespeare's plays were really written by Sir Francis Bacon." Who would ever listen if I just said, "I believe . . . ?" Another way of taking the weight of credibility off my shoulders was to say, obnoxiously, "*One might think. . . .*" That ubiquitous "one" used to be omnipresent in books of etiquette. It was synonymous with the people who count, and if I wanted to be worthy of notice, I would have to do what "one" did. Then there was the regal "we" that made me sound as if God were on my side, and I was far more than just one measly person. If my back were up against the wall I could always add a little self-importance and distance to my message by saying "you." "You always feel better after a cup of warm tea." As if I knew how you felt.

The first step in disentangling this muddle of stances, self-images and learned but habitual misrepresentation is speak in the first person. Speak for yourself. Say, "I." There is some risk in speaking for yourself. Notice whether this direct way of talking feels more exciting, more on target. *Spend a whole day speaking only in the first person.*

Part of the confusion we feel around each other is that we have learned how to mask our real feelings. We smile when we are really angry or hurt. Sometimes we use voice tone. When exasperated, I may say sweetly, "Please close the door." But I am leaving out much of the message. I mean to say, "When you leave the door open like that, the draft make the room chilly, and I have to interrupt what I'm doing to pay attention to it and it drives me bananas. But I am trying to concentrate on this recipe and I don't want to risk getting into a long conversation, which I fear would happen if I make my irritation known.''

2. *Watch yourself for incongruities among your feelings, manner and tone of voice. Write down the unspoken messages:* Because we have learned to pay so much attention to words and to disregard body language, energies and other messages, we are easily confused. Unlike any healthy cat, dog or housefly, we disregard important messages like smell, because people aren't supposed to smell.

And we aren't supposed to admit that we notice blushing, tension, pallor, sweating, or any of the other visible signs of inner states. This confusion is exaggerated by the inaccuracy with which people use words. For instance, most people do not discriminate between thought, belief, opinion and feeling. If I tell you that ''I feel you ought to . . .'' I am not stating a feeling. If you can put a ''that'' after a statement, it is probably not a feeling but an opinion in disguise. Spend a day noticing the difference between thought and feeling. Give yourself five points every time you spot a disguised opinion or a physical manifestation that belies your words. It means you are becoming more sensitive and harder to manipulate.

## EMOTIONAL-VOCABULARY EXERCISE

We are rich in feelings that flow underneath the surface of our awareness. Strangely, most of us don't have a sufficient vocabulary of feeling to express the subtlety of our inner experience. We end up frustrated or sounding somewhat primitive: ''Wow. Great.''

Make a list of words for feeling states. This can be fun. See how many feeling words you can list. It will help you communicate more accurately as you verbalize your feelings to others.

Communication is a discipline, an art. Just because we have been talking all our lives doesn't mean we know how to communicate. Clarity comes with practice. It takes attention and a willingness to be receptive to change. The alternative is to remain bound and disturbed by the recurrent misunderstandings and the sense of isolation that are inevitable when communication is incomplete and unclear.

Following are some exercises and suggestions to help you become more understandable. It's best to work with a partner or partners. You can deepen a friendship by practicing together.


## DEEPEN A FRIENDSHIP

The following format will give you guidelines for a situation that causes you discomfort:

State what you are responding to: the situation.
State your feelings.
State the consequences.

Make up a situation if there are no current exasperations handy. For example: Your friend cut out in the middle of a telephone conversation and said she would call you back—but she never did. You were disappointed, perhaps, and felt abandoned. You could say: "When you didn't call me back the other night, I felt disappointed. I thought you had forgotten me, and then I began feeling angry. Because I was angry I didn't call you for two days."

Most of us assume that all this interior information is magically understood by our friends, relatives and colleagues. Although people do sense feelings and incongruities, most people never figure out what's really going on in the other person's mind.

Another example:

"When you wag your finger at me and raise your voice, I think I'm being scolded and I feel defensive and want to withdraw."

At first this exercise may require some effort and a lot of concentration. You're probably voicing feelings you don't usually disclose. You're saying what triggered them and how you're responding. You may wonder why there is so much emphasis on feelings. Even in the most public situations—at work, in the bank, at the store—where we are careful not to express emotion, there isn't much we can talk about that doesn't trigger an emotional response. However, we have been well trained to hide these responses from others, and even from ourselves. If we had no feelings about what we did we would probably feel bored and restless.

## HEAR ME WITH YOUR HEART

Expressed feelings allow us to feel accepted and intimate if they are received without judgment. This is the essence of relationship, of friendship. When my heart is heavy I want my listener to hear me completely, not cut me off with some pat advice or consolation. I want to feel free to cry without embarrassment. Most of all I want to feel understood. Then I feel cared for. How close I feel, how cared for, depends on my feeling understood—and understanding myself.

Not being listened to—a common experience for many people—

can reverberate throughout life. One woman remembered an incident that took place when she was 16. It was New Year's Eve and she was all dressed up in evening clothes waiting for her boyfriend. He never came. He never called. As evening became night and she decided she had been stood up she ran to her bedroom to cry. She was humiliated, furious, and totally abandoned. "I thought I was the ugliest, most unlovable girl in the world. I thought I had been abandoned forever. My heart was swollen and breaking." Her family were playing cards in the living room as if nothing had happened. "I felt abandoned by them, too. They didn't even care enough to ask how I felt or listen to me. After that I felt very separate from them. I never again told them anything that mattered to my heart."

In my own life I can recall many moments when a little communication would have made me feel cherished instead of isolated. When I was divorced I felt desolate. I didn't expect anyone to solve my problems but I wished someone cared enough to listen to my feelings. One friend had remarked, "Oh, you'll get over it and have a new love before long." Another reminded me, "Well you never were happy together." I felt belittled, silenced, and even scolded. I wished I hadn't told them. My father heard the news. I waited. I was hoping he would say something that would make me feel close. Silence. He heard the news as if there was nothing to say. I felt unfinished.

Still another person tried to cajole me out of my unhappiness, joking, and pointing out that misery only breeds misery. At that point I believed my feelings were so unimportant to these key people in my life that I must be unimportant to them. Each one undoubtedly cared for me but must have felt so uncomfortable with my feelings that they reacted by trying to kid me or by turning away. For a while after that I felt more alone when I was with my family than when I was alone. It seemed my real nature and feelings had to be locked away for me to be acceptable.

Have you ever felt that way? Write out some of the situations in which you felt unheard by your family or friends.

Even in the SAGE office among people devoted to improving communication while working with a coach, we did not have an easy time. We found we had deeply ingrained habits that stood in our way. Sometimes we were pressed for time and we chose to meet a deadline rather than listen to a colleague. Sometimes I would have too much on my mind and heart to become empty enough to listen. Listening requires all of your attention.

To help out we adopted some guidelines from *Leadership Effectiveness Training* by Thomas Gordon. When someone comes to you with a problem, in trouble, or in intense emotion, you may want to recall these guidelines to enhance your ability to listen. Listening with no judgments, no distracting inner dialogue, is the biggest gift you can give. The following are based on guidelines from Thomas Gordon.

## DON'T

1. *Order, direct, command:* Telling others to do something—"Stop talking and start doing the dishes"—tells them their feelings and needs are not important, that they must comply with your wishes. Usually such messages produce fear and resentment, and the other person may fight back, resist or test your will.

2. *Warn, admonish, threaten:* Telling others what consequences will ensue if they do something *you* don't think is right—"If you get divorced at this age, you'll have to raise your children

alone"—often elicits a response such as "I don't care. I still feel this way."

3. *Moralize, preach, evoke obligation:* Telling others what they should or shouldn't do—"You shouldn't behave this way"— produces guilt that presses an external power, authority or obligation. It may make the other person feel you do not trust his or her judgment or values.

4. *Advise, give suggestions or solutions:* Telling others how to solve their problems—"Why don't you tell your boss . . ."—may make you feel you are being helpful, but it may also make them feel inferior and wonder why they didn't think of that solution. Your suggestions may be excellent, but you haven't allowed the other person the dignity of working out his or her problem, and the result can be resentment.

5. *Try to persuade with logic, argument, instruction, lecturing:* Trying to influence others with facts, counterarguments, logic or your own opinions may make them feel inadequate, defensive and resentful. Even if you have information you think the other person lacks, people hate to be proved wrong and will often defend their positions to the bitter end. You may know that "the facts show marijuana use produces early aging," but the other person may view this as a harangue and may simply discount what you say or assume an "I don't care" attitude.

6. *Judge, criticize, disagree, blame, make negative judgments or evaluations:* These messages more than any others make people feel inadequate, inferior, stupid and unworthy. Self-concepts are shaped by judgments and evaluations. "It's your fault; you're so stubborn." "It never would have happened if you weren't so timid." Evaluation quickly influences people to keep their feelings to themselves. They know it isn't safe to talk to you about subjects that mean anything to them. Even if they feel the evalu-

ation is correct, they may become angry and full of animosity, because negative evaluation is destructive.

7. *Excessively praise, agree or approve:* If you praise others too effusively, they may well assume you are insincere and manipulative.

8. *Name-call, ridicule, shame:* Making others feel foolish, stereotyping or categorizing them has a totally negative effect on their self-image.

9. *Interpret, analyze, diagnose:* Telling others what their motives are, or analyzing why they do or say something, communicates that you have them "figured out." If your conclusion is accurate, the person may feel exposed; if it is wrong (as is most often the case), he or she will probably become angry. By implying "I can see through you," you cut off further messages; the other person feels put down and refrains from sharing his or her feelings with you.

10. *Reassure, sympathize, console or support by minimizing:* Trying to make others feel better by belittling their problems or underestimating the seriousness of them, by attempting to make others' feelings "go away," denies the depth of those feelings. If someone has just lost a spouse or a job, or has just been diagnosed as having a catastrophic illness, the *last* thing he or she needs to hear is how much worse others have it or something like "Everything will seem better tomorrow."

11. *Probe, question, interrogate:* Trying to determine reasons, motives and/or causes for others' problems can convey that you are suspicious or doubtful of them. People who are troubled don't usually talk because they want you to solve their problems for them, but as a way of finding their own solutions. Children are particularly vulnerable, since adults almost always end up telling them what to do. Moreover, when you question people as they re-

late a problem, your questions limit their freedom to talk it all out and thereby possibly *see* the solution.

12. *Withdraw, distract, humor:* Attempting to get others' minds away from the problem, withdrawing from the problem yourself, offering distractions, kidding others about their feelings, pushing others' problems aside can indicate that you are not interested in them, that you don't respect their feelings or that you reject them outright. Putting a person—adult *or* child—off or diverting his or her attention may seem to succeed for the moment, but a postponed problem is not a solved problem; and if you brush it aside, the other person soon learns to take his or her important feelings and problems elsewhere.

All of the above response types communicate nonacceptance, yet all are common. How many of them are you guilty of?

There are alternative ways of responding.

## DO

1. *Be a silent, passive listener:* Listening without verbally responding can give a powerful message. Sometimes all others need is to be heard. Passive listening communicates acceptance if you give undivided attention, setting aside all other tasks and concentrating on the other person's words. The only drawback to listening silently is that the speaker doesn't know if he or she has been understood, so look into the speaker's eyes as he or she talks.

2. *Make simple acknowledgments:* Noncommittal responses such as "Oh" or "I see" let others know you are tuned in to them yet pass no judgment, make no evaluation.

3. *Open the door:* Verbal responses that invite others to say

more—"Tell me about it" or "I'd like to hear more about that"—encourage them to continue. Such words leave your feelings out of the communication, but indicate that you are willing and ready to listen.

4. *Listen actively:* Active listening is the process of decoding others' words and feeding them back to verify that you have understood. Do not inject your own feelings, evaluation, logic, advice, analysis or questions; repeat or paraphrase only what the message says to you. This helps a person express him- or herself freely, and may even be a catharsis to troublesome feelings. A person who feels that you really hear him or her will feel warm and close to you. After being heard through, thinking out a problem aloud, the other person will be more willing to listen to your ideas and thoughts.

## LISTENING EXERCISE

The following exercise allows you to practice being the kind of listener everyone—including you yourself—needs. It is an exercise in observing yourself, in watching how much you impose yourself on others even when you are trying to be helpful and open. All of us do it. In going through this exercise repeatedly I began to see that I had made a career out of advising and suggesting, putting myself in a teacher role. It made me rather uncomfortable to discover how much I did this to the people around me, and I began to understand better why they responded as they did. The exercise thus allows us to practice and evaluate our listening ability.

1. When you and your partner(s) meet for a session, say hello, but postpone social conversation until later. Find a place to sit

where you can comfortably face each other and see each other's eyes. Start by closing your eyes and taking five deep breaths, relaxing and feeling your entire body.

2. Decide who will speak first and who will listen. The speaker will talk for 10 minutes, then rest for a minute or two in silence. Then the other person(s) will speak for 10 minutes each.

3. *Listener(s):* Sit in a calm, receptive, meditative state of mind. Just listen. Do not visibly react. Don't judge or comment. Don't even smile, nod or grunt. Listen openly, without criticism. Try to listen as if *you* were the speaker. It may help to imagine putting all your personal concerns in a box for safekeeping until the speaker has finished.

4. *Speaker:* Don't try to interact or persuade your partner, just speak. Acknowledge your own feelings and allow yourself to speak, realizing that you are really being heard. Be totally immersed in yourself.

5. Between monologues take more deep breaths.

6. When both or all partners have spoken, take a half hour or an hour to discuss your observations. Be as honest as you can. Describe your feelings as you spoke or listened. Your feelings tell a great deal and may help both or all of you understand yourselves.

What did this exercise mean to you?

Did you gain any new insights into yourself? your partner(s)?

How do you feel now?

Were you hiding feelings during the exercise?

How about your feelings toward your partner(s)?

## Possible Topics

1. How do I postpone satisfaction in my life?

For example: Do I think things will be better, more pleasant, more rewarding in the future? Am I waiting for some outside event to occur? Am I always preparing for the future, taking care of family, planning entertainment? Do I forget to stop and experience what is hapening now?

2. How could each moment of my life become satisfying?

For example: If I stopped worrying about the future. . . . If I stopped thinking and had a quiet mind. . . . If I weren't so timid about asking for what I want. . . . If I weren't so polite and I dared. . . .

3. What is it I say I want that, in my heart, I know I *don't* want?

For example: To be responsible and take care of everyone. To improve my marriage. To be a model grandparent. To have a new home, to live to be 100, to be young again.

4. What things about myself do I hide from myself and others?

For example: My nasty temper, critical nature, sexual taste, lack of compassion, impatience, despair, sense of insecurity, sense of superiority, sloppiness, fear of being disliked. We hide the things we think others will dislike or reprimand us for, and when we hide we are alone. Sharing the things we hide shows us they are not so unusual; that we do not have to be ashamed of or secretive about them.

5. What is my self-image? Is there a difference between the image I present to the world and what I feel is my real self?

For example: I act like a secure, forceful, agreeable person— but really I am uncertain. I seem gregarious, but really I like to be alone and I am shy. I act more insecure than I am so people will pity me or give me leeway.

Living up to a self-image is imprisoning. It deprives us of freedom and therefore robs us of closeness with others.

## REPEATED-QUESTIONS EXERCISE

Sometimes we can only dig out deeper answers by asking the same question repeatedly. This exercise is immensly helpful in dealing with topics we think we know all about.

Decide who will question first and who will answer.

1. *Answerer:* Allow yourself to become totally immersed in your own feelings and thoughts, knowing your partner is listening with complete attention.

2. *Questioner:* Remain in a meditative, quiet state of mind. Do not react with nods, grunts or other gestures. Just ask your question, then listen to the answer. When the speaker has finished, say "Thank you," and *repeat* the question in a firm, gentle voice.

3. Keep a piece of paper beside you, and at the end of each answer jot down a key word or phrase that will allow your partner to recapture his or her answers later.

4. Stop after 15 minutes or when your partner has answered the question as many times as you consider sufficient. There will be a change in the answers: laughter, a strong feeling, a sudden loss of interest, or an expression of insight. This change tells you the exercise has accomplished its work.

5. Switch roles.

6. When both of you have answered the questions, give the key words and phrases you listed to your partner to help in your discussion of the exercise.

## Questions to Be Repeated: Choose One Per Session

1. What keeps you stuck doing things the same way, feeling the same feelings?
2. Who are you?

These exercises may allow you to deepen a friendship that is already well established. They can help you come into deeper contact with someone you know or someone you have just met.

IT IS VERY IMPORTANT NOT TO LET THE EXERCISES BECOME SOCIAL CONVERSATION; SAVE YOUR SOCIALIZING UNTIL AFTER YOU HAVE FINISHED THE EXERCISES.

# CHAPTER 9

# DREAMS AND SLEEP

The group's intimacy deepened even more when we began to share our dreams. We had been prompted to record them by an artist who was writing a dissertation on dream interpretation. At first many of us thought we did not remember our dreams, and most reported dreaming very little. Nonetheless we agreed to write down whatever fragments we recalled when we awakened in the morning, and to record whatever moods we felt.

We began somewhat tentatively, but soon found we didn't need much to get a clue to our inner processes.

"I went out of the house and down the road. I saw a bicycle and it was broken. . . ."

That was all one man remembered.

Now we began to view the fragments we remembered in the manner of gestalt psychologist Fritz Perls. Perls offered no symbols, no theory, no interpretation, only a point of view: Everything in your dream is you! To understand the dream you need only rephrase it as if you were the director of that inner play. Make every noun a part of yourself. In this way you can begin to see the rich meaning of even a small fragment.

"I sent myself out of the house-part-of-myself and down the road-part-of-myself. I saw a bicycle-part-of-myself, but it was a broken bicycle-part-of-myself."

The man whose dream it was began to smile broadly. He figured out his own dream.

"That is the way I feel." He had a sense of being closed in by his family, of wanting to be on the road, unrestricted, free. But his vehicle—his body—was in need of work. Although this one-sentence fragment seemed innocuous on the surface, it expressed a deep feeling of frustration, longing and vitality.

It does not take years of psychoanalysis to explore the messages your dreams send you every night. Nor can anybody else understand them as well as you can yourself. They are messages *from* you *to* you. They are like letters to yourself from the part of you that is deeply buried, hidden, ignored, maybe feared. Carl Jung, who spent most of his life analyzing his patients' dreams, found that dreams spoke of unconscious feelings so deep and so hidden that some came out of the collective memory of the human race. He proclaimed that only the dreamer can fully know the meaning of the message in the dream. To accept somebody else's interpretation is to accept another person's theory about you.

## EXPLORING YOUR DREAMS

You can use this same process by writing down your dreams.

1. Keep a notebook and pen or a tape recorder beside your bed. When you expect to recall dreams you are more likely to do so.

2. When you awaken, move very slowly. Let yourself lie and recall. Wait. Dreams are like movies on clouds: They evaporate if rushed or pushed.

3. Write down anything you recall. The tiniest fragments are useful. If you write down how your body feels and what mood you are in you have a lot of information even if you recall no dream fragments at all.

4. Look at the fragment, the mood and the body feeling. Your dream may contain events from yesterday and a straightforward message for you. It may even tell you something you need to do.

5. Rewrite your dream so that you put the words ''part of myself'' after every noun. In addition to the clear message, a dream conceals information like an iceberg. Most of it is invisible at first. The gestalt method of rephrasing a dream allows you to start reaching for the hidden meanings. Everything you dream comes out of your brain, after all. It is your private movie projection. It comes from your memory, your body, your perceptions, filtered and changed by your particular personality. This is why when you rewrite a dream you make yourself everything in it.

It may seem very clumsy to reword dreams that way. And it may not seem very revealing at first. Still, as you do it you will begin to see something magical about the way your feelings and your mind work in images; how you experience the very ordinary items of daily life—your room, cutlery, books, clothes, food—as part of yourself.

During our first sessions on dreams many members of the group began to offer theirs, but one stood out in all our minds. It spoke for us all.

''I'm standing in a shady valley. Across the valley is a narrow path high on the side of a mountain. The path is cut by three narrow, deep streams that become waterfalls after they cross the path.

There are three lovely red wool blankets laid across the streams as bridges. Are they magically strong enough to carry me safely across, or are they a trap that will let me fall to my death?''

During relaxation sessions we had used some red-and-orange mohair blankets to cover people. They were so soft and spectacularly colorful that the members of the group often commented on them. With that piece of information you can begin to see the meaning of this dream.

I have myself look across the shady valley-part-of-myself to a narrow path-part-of-myself, on a high side-part-of-myself of a mountain-part-of-myself. The path-part-of-myself is cut by three narrow, deep streams-part-of-myself that become waterfalls-part-of-myself after they cross the path-part-of-myself. There are three lovely red wool blankets-part-of-myself. Are they strong enough to carry me across or will they let me fall to my death-part-of-myself?

As she began talking about the path, the streams and the blankets, the dreamer became more emotional. She was unfolding many of the fears our process brought to the surface in all of us. Were the comfort and excitement and promise of our group's work something fragile that would collapse under our weight and send us plunging to annihilation?

Quite a few people in the group began to express similar fears. As one woman put it, "I've spent 74 years creating my identity, and you are asking me to throw it away or abandon it. And I find I'm doing that! I'm changing! But I have to tell you it's hard!"

There wasn't anyone in the room who didn't share some of that tension and fear. To grow is to change. To make room for change we have to drop and forget some past habits, some parts of ourselves. Before each growth phase some small part of us must die.

Once we have allowed ourselves to break a habit we may feel lost, at sea for a little while. We have not yet formed our new behavior and feelings, and the transition can be very frightening. It is the same transition working people face upon retiring, the transition parents face when children leave home. In later life every loss or potential loss brings about the death of a part of oneself.

All this was expressed in the dream of the red blankets with which the dreamer had been covered and warmed during many emotional sessions. In the dream she wondered whether these promises of growth would allow her to move through the valley. Or was that hopeful part of herself a trap, the vision of great heights and light a false promise?

We shared that question. As any of us clear out the restrictive, negative, conditioned habits of mind and feeling, we come closer to home, to something deep in our natures. Some people call it "God." It is the greater Reality of which our lives are such a tiny fragment, the greater Reality that gives meaning and purpose to our lives. Yet at the level of everyday sorrow and struggle we had no pat answers. The dreamer wondered why her cancer-ridden husband lingered on. He was dying and her feelings were mixed: sorrow, pity, impatience. Her frankness laid her open to the anger of people in the group. She did not pretend to love nursing her husband, or to wish him to last longer. She was hopeful, yet she was also doubtful that anything she did left her any better off.

That summer her husband died and she began to work with Ken Dychtwald, teaching in a home for the elderly. A year and a half later she had moved to another city and was beginning to teach groups of professionals how to work with the elderly. She had become aware of herself as an energetic, free, happy woman. She even wrote an article saying that life began at 76. One might call this a happy ending, except for the fact that life is not fixed and there are no permanent states of being.

Transitions are usually difficult. The woman's decision to move was a hard one. The night before she was to catch her plane to a new life she fell and broke her hip. The accident said all she herself had not said about the difficulty of leaving. Still she had already got herself in good physical condition, so she healed rapidly and was able to leave six weeks later. Who knows whether that accident was necessary? A therapist could speculate that if the woman had really worked on her dreams, expressed more of her feelings of ambivalence, fear and insecurity, perhaps she would not have fallen on the eve of her departure. Speculation is useless, of course—yet as we went on to further explore our dreams, we began to see how the information they gave us might save us from having to experience unconscious events, like accidents, in waking life.

Our next step, suggested by an artist, led us to re-create our dreams for the entire group so that each of us experienced the dreams of the others as if they were our own. Occasionally somebody dreamed something important to all of us and this sharing made us one dreamer.

The method of allowing another person to dream your dream is simple, and it works with one listener or twenty.

## SHARING-A-DREAM EXERCISE

1. Make sure your listener(s) is comfortable—preferably lying down with eyes closed. Get him or her to relax. You might use one of the exercises described in this book, or a breathing exercise. Or

make up a technique. Your listener should be deeply relaxed but not asleep as you talk.

2. Tell your dream vividly, as if it were happening in the present. You might enhance the recounting by closing your eyes and redreaming it as you speak.

3. When you finish, leave a few moments for your listener(s) to react. Then ask how he or she dreamed the dream and what it meant to him or her.

One man told of a dream I will always remember. If I didn't have a transcript of the session proving that it was his dream, I might be persuaded I had dreamed it myself. It stood out as a mythic dream, a fable of what we were all trying to do as we changed our habits and our lives. His dream narrative:

"There was a field and a 14- to 15-foot-long snake was coming toward me. I was looking at it and something told me I couldn't move as fast as it could, so there was no use running away from it. It kept coming toward me, and I wondered whether or not it was poisonous. I couldn't figure that out. I looked around for some sort of weapon and the ground was bare. I looked down and all I had on were shorts. I thought I would have to fight the snake and take my chances. As it got really close to me, I saw it had yellow tentacles with a small head on each one. It was coming closer to me, and I braced to deal with it.

"The snake arched its head and looked at me. There was a little creek, so I backed to the other side of it, thinking the snake was coming for water. It was coming in a direct line toward me. As it got about five feet from me it pulled back its head and all those tentacles came out that I hadn't noticed before. It looked menacing. Then I woke up.

"I sat up. I could almost see the snake, the dream had been so vivid and in color. I didn't want to dream about it again but I couldn't put it out of my mind. I got up and walked around the house and came back to bed. I thought about the dream quite a bit and I tried to recall what my reactions were as it developed. I've never been particularly afraid of snakes.''

As the people who had heard the dream sat up many of them looked stunned.

"You were really confronting danger," remarked one man.

"I can tell you how I see it," said the dreamer. "I feel some part of me is moving too fast. It's coming closer to my core. As it comes closer it feels menacing and I want to fight it. As it gets closer it multiplies—as if some part of me is changing."

"That was heroic. You were about to slay a dragon."

Surely there was a heroic quality in the dream that all of us recognized. The snake—symbol of a search for forbidden knowledge—was there for all of *us*, too, as we continued our work together, digging deeper into ourselves, exposing more of our true selves and facing the changes we were bringing about in our lives as we admitted to ourselves what we really felt. Most of us had been living lives we only half wanted, or that contained elements we constructed out of earlier needs. Now we were stuck with them—unless we were willing to confront the danger and act like the dreamer and take a stand.

Often when we stopped analyzing and simply thought about the richness of our dream experience, we were awed. Did we really have access to the whole of human experience in our dreams? Could we experience all the basic, archetypical images—those of birth and death, of the hero's journey, of not only racial consciousness but the primitive organic stages of evolution?

As we continued to share our dreams every two weeks or so,

people who hardly remembered dreaming before began to recount long and involved stories.

Sometimes, to discover some of the hidden emotional meanings, the dreamer would act out the different parts of the dream.

## ACTING-OUT-A-DREAM EXERCISE

1. Write down whatever you remember of your dream.
2. Imagine you are each object in your dream. Really put yourself into feeling what it would be like to be the house, the key in the lock, the front step under your foot, and so on. Acting out each part of a dream may prove to be one of the most satisfying ways of discovering yourself. If you are sharing your dreams with someone, this process becomes a very real process of sharing yourself.

Dream-sharing in this fashion was perhaps the first experience one group had of openly showing deep feelings. A visiting therapist asked for a participant willing to risk sharing his or her feelings. Eugenia, our group leader, volunteered. She told of a dream of dropping her pocketbook into a muddy pool and diving in with her clothes on to search for it.

"What is it like to be the pocketbook?"

"You hold my keys and my security," Eugenia said.

Then she began to experience the pocketbook-part-of-herself, lost on the bottom of a muddy pool-part-of-herself. Soon tears were falling down her face, and one woman rushed to hold her protectively. Other members of the group also looked upset and angry.

"I cry very easily," she explained. She pointed out that she had not really understood the meaning of her dream until she began to act it out and feel the deeper feelings. When her feelings came to the surface she began crying.

Many people went away from that session upset. Two years later it stood out in their minds as a milestone. Why were they upset? "I'm just afraid of feelings. We never showed feelings in my family." Yet feelings are the electricity, the energy in our dreams. Mere images would hardly be memorable. Feelings are the energy in life. They are complete messages at each moment, but they are transitory.

After that day many of us were able to express ourselves more freely, to cry if we wanted to, or express anger. Although it seemed upsetting at first the group agreed that this session gave everyone permission to feel and express strong emotions. This was the depth they had been hoping for. Older people in groups often said that though they were fatigued by confrontation, they also wanted excitement, energy, hope and growth. People often assume that older people want to remain protected, to be sheltered from ever feeling anything. That assumption is false. People who are not accustomed to expressing emotion are shy at first, but repeated practice in a secure group has changed suppressive habits. We no longer need to be so polite, to withhold our real selves from each other. As we share our dreams we are sharing our innermost selves.

Dreams can be a way of deepening our understanding and sharing with others. There are also methods for consciously directing your dreams to reveal solutions to problems, to tell you what you need to know. The Senoi tribe of Malaysia is reported to have based its society on the sharing of dreams; to have selected leaders by their dreams, and to have generated an unusually peaceful way of life. This group is cited in Patricia Garfield's book, *Creative Dreaming*.

## PERCHANCE TO DREAM

One winter afternoon a member of the group asked me why we dream. She knew I had written a book on sleep 10 years earlier. I had written it from scientific consciousness. I remembered standing, excitedly, in laboratories where people slept all night with tiny electrodes on their scalps, wires leading to a console that showed their heart rates, eye movements and brainwaves.

In the early 1960s it was discovered that about every 90 minutes during sleep a person moves his or her eyes as if looking at something. The breathing and heart rate change, becoming more irregular. Hormones surge. Males get erections. The body seems excited. These phenomena were found to exist in all mammals. If awakened during these rapid-eye-movement periods, people— even those who say they never dream—almost always recall dreaming. Not that they don't dream in between, but during these periods there are vivid dreams, often starting with mundane, short episodes early in sleep then moving into more bizarre, colorful, wild dreams.

New theories of dreaming attempt to explain what goes on at the cellular level in our brains during sleep. But no single theory could hope to cover the purpose of dreaming, which seems to be so threaded into the purpose of life. I now look back on the simple concepts of mind-brain-and-consciousness I had when I was writing scientifically and marvel at how inadequate they were in explaining the mysterious dimensions of our inner lives and of the nature of our minds.

How could we explain the dreams and visions ordinary people have used to educate themselves in unusual skills? How could I explain the tailor who learned psychiatry from a dead psychiatrist, or the person whose virtuosity on the piano came from "a spirit guide"? The objective physiological explanations of our need to dream simply cannot help us explore the nature of our consciousness.

In some of the disciplines of ancient India, dreams, sleep and waking consciousness were treated as one. Laboratory scientists have often described delta-stage sleep as oblivious. Most of us, if awakened from this phase of sleep, will be disoriented, not remember anything, and say it was oblivious sleep. But we are Westerners. We use our minds as we have been taught. Nobody ever taught us to make a connection between waking consciousness and deepest sleep.

In the late 1960s Swami Rama allowed Drs. Elmer and Alyce Green to wire him up and test him at the Menninger Clinic in Topeka, Kansas. In one experiment Swami Rama quickly entered sleep and snored away in his chair. In her soft voice Alyce Green repeated innocuous statements, such as "It's raining today but it may be sunny tomorrow." Swami Rama slept a while, then he awoke. He said this was for him like a state of recording. When he sat up and opened his eyes he would play back what had happened during his snores and delta brainwaves. He repeated all the sentences, and remembered telephones ringing in the room upstairs and footsteps of people moving. Yet he was totally rested.

## DREAM YOGA

There is a discipline, known sometimes as dream yoga, that can help create a greater continuity between waking consciousness and sleeping consciousness.

As you are falling asleep, maintain the image of a candle burning. See the flame. Prolong the time, and as you begin to fall asleep see the flame growing more distant. The longer you can see the flame, and the more aware you become of the transition into sleep, the closer you will come to bridging that gap between waking consciousness and "sleep."

Even if you do not have the persistence to practice this exercise every night, you will begin to understand something about the arbitrary boundaries we set on consciousness. Dreaming is vivid. Perhaps our dreams represent our real consciousness, while waking requires only our superficial attention.

A lot of our nightly work could be done while awake. Jack Schwarz, a naturopath and spiritual teacher with profound powers of vision, has shared with many people his own method for cutting the psychic drudgery out of sleep. Jack sleeps only an hour or two a night. He does not wrestle with unconscious problems as most of us do in our dreaming. He clears each day as he goes. In his book, *Voluntary Control*, he outlines a method all of us could use. I have found it extremely helpful, and it is very simple.

## NIGHTLY REVIEW

Before you go to sleep, reserve half an hour or an hour to review your day. Close your eyes and get deeply relaxed. Imagine you are watching a giant movie screen. Relive everything you did during the day. Watch your actions. What did you feel? Scrutinize even trivial events, thoughts or feelings that might be harmful. Ask yourself: "Did I do any harm today? If so, how can I repair it?"

You may feel you insulted someone or hurt someone's feelings. Apologize. Some harms might be hidden from others. You can repair them within yourself. For instance, were you dishonest with yourself or others? Did you have nasty thoughts about someone? Did you say something nice, but feel very resentful? Before you go to sleep you can rectify these negatives in your mind just by recognizing them. You will be doing some of the work that usually occupies your sleep. Then you can go to sleep with a clearer conscience.

You may find that the quality of your sleep changes if you go through this nightly review. Often we awake unrested, as if we have battled all night long. It seems strange; nothing dramatic happened during that day. Still, if we were to look over the trend of our lives we might perceive that we are in deep subterranean conflict about complaints we don't express. If we could begin to deal consciously with these feelings each night, not only might we feel more rested, we might need less sleep.

## CHANGING SLEEP PATTERNS

Many people think they need eight hours' sleep, and that they will always sleep as they did when young. When they sleep less they torture themselves about it.

As our group shared our dreams we discovered that sleep patterns change with age. It was clear that not one person over 60 slept through the night as he or she had when young. But what different attitudes we had! One man lay in bed smiling at the jokes of the all-night disc jockey, relaxed and enjoying himself. A woman got up, drank coffee and read until she got sleepy, then in the wee hours went back to bed. Another woman felt lonely and depressed because she was awake in the darkness; she didn't want to disturb her husband, and found reading in bed unsatisfying. Some people got up and walked around. Some drank hot milk. Some fidgeted. "I do my roll breathing," said one woman. "I lie in bed and do about fifteen cycles of breathing. Sometimes I relax enough to go back to sleep. Mostly I'm just relaxed and that gives me enough rest. I don't sleep more than two to four hours a night."

Many of us, myself included, were brought up to believe we would be a wreck the next day if we didn't get our full night's sleep. So a night without sleep, and we panic. Our culture treats broken sleep as insomnia, an anathema, a pathology. We are told to take sleeping pills and treat ourselves to oblivion. Even scientific theory corroborates this disease attitude: One theory holds that our brain chemistry becomes depleted as we age, thus we begin to have broken sleep. Older people who complain about loneliness or depression during nighttime awakening are treated as if they are sick, given tranquilizers and sedatives. Unfortunately the resulting sleep is attended by side effects from the drugs. One man in our group told that while taking a tranquilizer he felt much less alert, and had thought he was losing his memory until he stopped the drug. By treating our changing sleep as an illness and medicating ourselves in order to sleep we may be missing the meaning of our symptoms.

Perhaps there is a reason for being awake as we advance in age. Our physiology may be guiding us toward greater awareness and growth despite the negativity of our culture. Surely it is an interesting coincidence that the early hours of morning, when older people said they were awake, happen to be the same hours that have been selected as optimum for meditation and inward reflection. In ashrams throughout the Orient, and in the West too, young people are struggling out of bed at three or four in the morning to meditate. Ironically it is the young who are attempting to follow a spiritual path before they have lived their lives.

In many Asian cultures, as well as among our own American Indians, it is generally understood that a person should live out his or her mature family and community life before taking up serious spiritual disciplines. Thus a person might begin at age 50 waking purposefully in the predawn atmosphere to meditate. This is a time when the electric mantle of Earth is more charged with negative ions than it is later in the day. Our consciousness is also different, for we have separated ourselves by sleep from our myriad daytime activities. We are rested. Our minds are perhaps freer of outside distractions, and we are closer to the mysterious underlayers of our beings.

Perhaps we could rename this period of nonsleep. Instead of calling it insomnia, an ailment, we might recognize the rich possibilities in the waking portions of the night.

Once a man in the group asked me, "What has been your greatest experience during the last three months?"

I remembered a night when I was deep in sorrow and tumult. As I lay sleeplessly in bed I was aware of a deep tranquility far beneath the violent surface. I lay there watching my feelings play themselves out as huge waves on a deep lake that was completely still on the bottom. This was not the kind of high point I had been taught to expect, but as I shared it I realized there was something vital in the experience that could never come from lectures, written words or any other external event.

## CHAPTER 10

# VISUALIZATION AND HEALING

"I lie in bed and have the most wonderful thoughts, and I think this is when I heal myself." The woman in the hospital bed smiled. She was pink-cheeked, radiant. Looking at her nobody would have believed she was 74 years old and had had a large malignancy removed from her intestine three day earlier. She had always been an extraordinary person, and now she was teaching us. Practicing relaxation, letting down barriers to intimacy, and using specific skills of concentration and visualization could in fact give a person unusual healing power in time of crisis. This woman had not developed her abilities overnight; she had been working at them for more than two years. The most important aspect of her recovery undoubtedly had to do with her beliefs.

Many of us grow up believing in a childlike way that a doctor will heal us if we get sick. We act as if our bodies were cars and we take them to specialists. If our liver is affected we go to a hematologist. If the problem is emotional we see a psychiatrist. It's as if our livers and minds were unconnected. In a crisis of faith we seek a member of the clergy. We think we will restore our overall health and balance in this divided fashion. Deep down we know that everything in our way of being is related—the way we think, feel, move, breathe, eat, make love, sleep, talk, work and day-dream. Our illness or health involves all of these. We also know we are connected to a larger reality, call it Nature or God, of which we are an insignificant part. It is this larger nature that heals us, not the surgery, psychological therapy, or drugs. None of them can make cells grow. None of them can infuse us with the vital energy of life.

Usually we pay no attention to our well-being until we have un-pleasant symptoms. Then we want relief. We do odd things. Imagine that you treated your car the same way you treat your body. You are driving along and the voltmeter begins to show a symptom. It oscillates and buzzes erratically. Instead of stopping everything to find out the cause, you paint it over and keep on driving. Everything is all right for a while, but the paint doesn't cover the irritating noise. So you stop at a service station and have it ripped out. Most of us would not treat our cars in this manner, yet we are often willing to use drugs or surgery this way on our-selves. Most car owners would stop for an overhaul. Yet how many body owners would stop their lives and make a real inner search of the components of their illness? The causes of our illness are hidden within the complexities of our being. This is a somewhat different view than we expect from Western medicine, but it can be found in Chinese and Indian medicine.

We have grown up expecting medicine to heal us by supplying the right injection, pill or surgery. These treatments often do get rid of the immediate symptoms, so we feel better. But next week or next month we find we have another ailment. We don't see them as related. Few of us take responsibility for the lifestyle that leads to these ailments. We know only that periodically we add a new symptom. Some become chronic. We have various logical explanations for this. We say influenza is caused by little beings known as viruses, but this doesn't explain why some people get sick and die in an epidemic while others don't even become ill.

## BELIEF: THE DIVINE HEALER

For lack of a better explanation, we could say the cause of illness is divine, and the healer is the same as the cause: divine. In ancient India, Egypt, Arabia and Greece healing was a spiritual process. It involved a change of attitude, or mind, known as metanoia. People went to healing centers where they meditated and underwent severe challenges until this change of heart could take place. All of us know of people who were supposed to die but miraculously survived. Sometimes they articulated some elusive but powerful inner transformation. There are many curiosities like these in medical literature. There is the case of a man in his 50s who went to the hospital for removal of a stomach cancer. The doctors opened him up, took one look, decided it was hopeless, and closed him up again. They sent him home. But they forgot to tell him he was hopeless. He assumed he was cured, that God had given him another chance, and he began to live his life differently in gratitude. He wasn't seen again until nine years later, when he had a coronary. There were no signs of cancer.

Belief is far more potent than we like to acknowledge. We pay lip-service to the idea that our thoughts create us, but at heart we deny it. Otherwise we would have to examine our thoughts carefully. We would ask how they affect us and others. What happens when we think angrily, in doubt or greed, or when we make small negative judgments that pass through our heads without causing external ripples? We like to imagine these thoughts are unseen, forgotten. But they are not forgotten by our minds *or* our bodies. Disease and healing are related to our deepest and most unadmitted ways of thinking and believing. This is why sharing those secrets, admitting them, seeing them, can be part of a healing process. After that they no longer have such a tight hold on us.

For many people a dramatic healing process begins with relaxing the inner guard against resisted ideas or mysteries. They can surrender to the natural sequence that is beyond the control of medical doctors or *any* human being. An attitude of surrender is not easy to acquire. Most of our blocks to healing probably come from inner resistance. It takes the form of tiny tensions in mind and body. For example, we do not allow our real feelings to show. We refuse to cry or show our fears and anguish. This containment can cause tension at a level too subtle to be immediately observable. Nonetheless it is there. We resist giving in to anesthesia, we cannot trust the very people in whose hands we have placed ourselves. At the deepest level we resist what is, thinking there is some evil in our distress, illness and death. We imagine that we should be in control of the overall life process. Resistance and tension act as amplifiers for pain and mental discomfort. When a person is able to give in to the ongoing process of his or her own life, surrendering to it and accepting whatever happens, that attitude is likely to accompany healing.

People sometimes come to that acceptance through religious inspiration, sometimes through a process of quieting and meditating. A healer is one who can in some way expedite the acceptance and healing process. Often this is a person with abundant selfless love, whose energy may give a sick person a boost, and whose presence can instill trust, acceptance, calm. In the early 1960s a small study indicated that surgical patients who opted to use hypnosis instead of anesthesia healed remarkably fast. The explanation seemed to be that they were unusually relaxed, trusting, and in a positive mental state due to hypnotic suggestion, in contrast to people who were not mentally prepared and went under anesthesia in a state of anxiety and tension.

As you have been reading this book and doing some of the exercises, you have been augmenting your own powers of self-healing. There are books that can carry you further. And you can practice some of the simple exercises in visualization others have found helpful.

Some of these exercises are undoubtedly ancient in origin. They must have been passed down from one shaman or family member to another for thousands of years. You are not likely to experience very dramatic results at first, but you will inevitably strengthen your ability to focus. It should become easier to sustain an internal image or point of concentration. This ability is a powerful tool. If you begin practicing while you feel well, it will become your ally in a time of crisis or pain. The following exercise is one you can practice with others or alone.

## HEALING-HANDS EXERCISE

1. Make certain that you will not be interrupted for an hour. Make yourself very comfortable, either sitting or lying down, but do not lean or lie on your hands.

2. Take five deep breaths. Pay attention to your breath so that

you feel it dividing as it enters your nostrils, goes down your throat and into your lungs. Feel the exhalation coming back up and out your nose or mouth. Relax deeply. Each time you exhale, allow yourself to drop outside thoughts, feelings, concerns.

3. Become acutely aware of your right hand. Feel its skeleton. If you don't feel it, imagine it. Imagine that you inhale, then exhale through the fingers of your right hand. Become very aware of each finger, and of the palm and back of your hand. When you feel a moving sensation in your hand, go on to the next step.

4. Become aware of your left hand, inhaling and exhaling through it. Be aware of the sensations in your fingers, in your palm, in the back of the hand. When you have vivid sensations, go on to the next step.

5. As you take a breath inhale through your right hand, up your right arm. Exhale down the left arm and out the left hand. Practice this until you feel a flow of sensation as you breathe and your arms begin to relax. They may feel long and heavy. Let go of any tight muscles. Let the breath warm and relax them.

6. Now feel the breath coming into your right hand and going out through your left hand as if it were making a circle through your body. Take slow, full, relaxed breaths.

7. Begin to feel your right hand having a lot of power. You can imagine that the left hand is exhaling leftovers while energy is building up in your right hand. You may feel some quivering or vibration. Feel the power building in your right hand.

8. Now notice some part of your body that doesn't feel good. Place your right hand about six inches above that spot. Continue to build the energy in your hand and transmit it to the part that feels bad. Your left hand is getting rid of wastes as you exhale through it. Discard those wastes. Do this for three minutes.

9. Stop and see whether there has been any change in the part of you that did not feel well.

10. Continue to build energy in your right hand and let go of wastes through your left hand. You can place that energized right hand above another ailing spot on your own body, or over someone else who is ill.

11. If someone is ill or aching, try building up the energy in your right hand and place it about six inches above the place he or she describes as sore, tight or tense. You can nourish him or her with your energy.

"I feel really foolish doing this," remarked one woman after a practice session. "It feels like a lot of hocus-pocus, yet I have to admit when I put my hand over my bad knee the pain went away. I just feel stupid holding my hand over someone else as if I were a magician or something."

"When I was doing this my hand was tingling like anything. It got really hot and I began to feel as if something was happening. It was exciting."

"I got some sensation in my hand at first, then I lost it. I couldn't get it back. I think I was distracted."

"When I held my hand over my partner I began to feel as if I weren't there any more, as if I were vanishing. It was terrifying."

As we did these exercises in groups there was a wide range of reactions. Everyone was excited. Some people were anxious as they worked with partners. They would forget their own boundaries and begin to feel formless and uncentered.

If you begin to feel that your own boundaries are disappearing, stop; concentrate on your feet and the energy at your navel. You need to retain your sense of boundaries. At the same time you need to leave your own problems, thoughts and feelings behind. This can be difficult at first; it requires patience. Practice focusing your energy, without a stream of thoughts and feelings, on someone who has asked for help. You need to be able to do the same thing for yourself. It can be difficult to stop thoughts and images and sustain focus. You can practice this at night lying in bed. Begin by sensitizing yourself, noticing the differences between yourself and all that surrounds you—the air, bedclothes, pillow, mattress. You can tune your hands, as you learned in the chapter on massage. Then move your hand like a radar screen over your body. Focus on the feelings in your hand and the parts of your body under it. If you lose focus and your mind wanders, bring yourself back. Treat yourself indulgently, as you would treat a dear child who has wandered off the garden path. Repeat this twice a day.

## LEARNING-TO-FOCUS EXERCISE

1. Allow yourself 10 minutes of tranquility every day. Find a quiet place where you will not be disturbed. Spend the time in serene contemplation. You might look at a plant, or a tree, or out the window. As you practice you will find you have fewer distractions and the quality of your experience will change.

After a while, if you practice this contemplation often enough, you can begin to look at an object without any thoughts at all. You can become totally immersed in caressing it with your eyes and attention. When you can become still enough to focus this way, you will find that even simple objects—a match stick, for example— become interesting, rich and full of meaning to you.

The next step comes once you have learned to maintain tranquility and focus for 10 minutes.

2. Look at yourself in the mirror as if you were looking at a stranger. Look at yourself as a stranger would see you—a stranger who has nothing at stake and sees you out of a deep calm.

Calm and detachment are particularly necessary when you are sick or in pain. In this state you won't drain your energy with bad feelings. Moreover, as you attain an attitude of inner calm, you can survey yourself and separate the essential from the nonessential. When I am under stress, irritable or lethargic, there is one visualization that really changes the picture. It popped into my mind spontaneously one day, and a number of people have found it helpful. Probably, in slightly different form, in has been used since ancient times.

## PERSPECTIVE-FROM-SPACE EXERCISE

1. Loosen clothing, anything tight; remove your glasses, watch, jewelry and shoes. Lie down with one pillow under your knees and another under your head. Pick a warm, quiet place where you can be alone, and a time when you can be uninterrupted even by pets. This exercise calls for very deep relaxation.

2. Sit in a comfortable armchair, or stretch out on a couch or bed and begin to relax by breathing deeply. Close your eyes. Breathe in through your hands and out through your toes. Breathe into your feet, your ankles, your calves. Breathe all the way up your legs into your abdomen, chest, shoulders, back. Feel the breath suffuse your head, relaxing your face. With each exhala-

tion relax more. Survey your entire body to see whether you are deeply relaxed. If you feel any spot of tension, breathe or imagine breathing warmth into that area until the sensation dissolves. When your body feels so relaxed you almost cannot feel it, go on to the next step.

3. Feel your body expanding, getting lighter and larger. Breathe in to a count of four. Hold for a count of twelve. Breathe out to a count of twenty. Each time you exhale, relax more. Exhale your crowded thoughts, tensions, worries. Inhale new energy.

4. Now, eyes closed, begin to imagine yourself sitting on a small platform about 2,000 feet above your house. You cannot fall off. The platform will not drop. You are secure. You are about to look down at your own life through a magic telescope. It will let you see through walls. It will let you see a week in a few minutes.

5. As you look down from the platform, first scan the geography around your home. What do you see? Where do you usually go? There is a whole terrain surrounding the home in which you live, the place you may work, and the places you usually go. Look down and map the usual routes you travel, the terrain on which you live most of your life. Do you usually travel the same routes to the same places, see the same people? Do you notice what lies in between? Do you repeat the same things over and over, or do you move around freely in your territory? How large is your domain? Do you always go down the same streets, look in the same stores, see the same people? Are there areas of beauty and interest nearby? Is there an invisible wall of habit and inertia enclosing your pattern of activity so that you have a smaller domain than you would like?

6. Now comes the important part. Turn your telescope down

on your house. Start as you get up in the morning. Watch yourself brushing your teeth, dressing; watch your thoughts. Is this what you want to think? You can speed up or slow down to have a close look at how you feel, move, spend your time; at how your life moves. Turn the telescope through the walls onto your own life patterns. What do you see? Spend plenty of time at this. Watch carefully. See yourself moving, walking, eating. How does it look to you? Is your self enjoying what it does? Is your self paying attention? Is your self eating thoughtlessly? Is your self listening to its real needs, or does it confuse wants with needs?

7. Watch for habits and repetitions. Watch for emotions that come up again and again. Whenever you see a repeated negative emotion, watch for a longer time. Do you repeat some behavior that generates a negative feeling?

8. Are there patterns of outgoingness and withdrawal? Do you have rhythms of restlessness, sleepiness?

9. What about people? Are your relationships unchanging? Are there things you could share with your friends and family that would change your relationships? Could you take some risks? Could you become more intimate? Are there people who could enrich your life whom you do not go out to see? Whom could you phone? To whom could you write?

The first time I did this exercise, I gasped with astonishment. I saw myself like a rat in a maze, repeating the very patterns I knew I didn't like. Nobody was forcing me to run the same track over and over; I did it like a robot. I lived in New York City in a fascinating region, but I restricted my activity to a few blocks and the people I saw were not the people I selected, but those I happened to meet on the way to the subway or when I accepted invitations. I saw that I did this in my relationships, too, consuming my time habitually, not out of conscious choice. I had constructed a kind of prison for myself that had the external appearance of a very exciting and free life. The prison was in my mind. Not only did I constrict my movements outside my apartment, I went through certain ritualistic motions at home. For example: To save housework, I told myself, I folded my clothes neatly. I never ran in, shed clothes, kicked my shoes across the floor and flung myself on the bed. I never thought of using my guest room as an art room, but neatly used my materials in the kitchen, carefully cleaning up after each session. I performed duties first: my work, then social calls, and finally—if there was anything left—what I wanted.

What was important in this life? That small figure in the apartment was sitting at the typewriter, shopping, traveling to Washington. She was staying neat, putting money in the bank, being nice to dates, mothering people, walking the dog. Ten years later it is not possible to reconstruct precisely the details of the vision. I felt myself exploding with the insight. Was that really my life? How could I have trapped myself to such an extent? It seemed simple to get out of the habits when I looked at my life in its surroundings rather than from within. From the vantage point of space I saw what inner freedom would have meant, what possibilities lay along my path, even inside my own living quarters. As I looked down and saw myself as a stranger might, observing the apartment, the city and all, I asked: "Why doesn't she get up from her typewriter and run in the park? Why doesn't she train that dog not to bother her?"

Almost six years later I listened to a man talking about his revelation from the exercise. He had seen that his attempts to retire from his life as a union leader had been ineffective.

He saw that he had potential friendships with men outside the union, that there were many enjoyable things to do in the world. What had held him in the bondage of routine? Why did he leave home so seldom? Why did he not see people he liked for lunch? His view from above showed rich possibilities all around. All he needed was to remember to lift the phone. He wasn't trapped by old age, but by his mindset.

## THE WAY OUT

The path out of an ingrown life and mindset often takes an unpredictable route. First you must see the situation; then you can expose yourself to new possibilities. One man who had been diffident and depressed took a professional massage course. He began working with young people at a crisis-counseling center, later with the elderly in a nursing home. He got out of his old routine, his rut. Once physically active, now living with a disability, he understood the wheelchair-bound nursing-home residents. He invented games for them. For one, he would come in with a basket of bright-colored balls of yarn, stand in the middle of the room and toss a ball: "Hey, Bessie, catch this!" The woman would laugh and toss it back, though she hadn't caught a ball in decades. Soon the room was alive with flying balls of yarn—and with laughter. The man had liberated the residents from their feelings of stagnation.

A number of our acquaintances found themselves escaping their ruts simply by sharing their new feelings and knowledge with others. They began teaching friends, or working with staff in nursing homes; they also continued to provide one another with moral support and stimulation. And they began talking about seeing their lives in new perspective.

As you try to visualize your own life in perspective, you may not see it vividly. You may not "see" it at all. There may be some nebulous feeling or image in the back of your mind, or you may "know" something. Don't worry: You'll see your life in a way that is right for you. Many people think they *can't* visualize. Yet most can imagine being in their bedroom, walking over to the bed and turning down the covers. In an earlier chapter you probably discovered how powerful visual images can be when you imagined tasting some lemon juice and noticed that you secreted more saliva. That, too, is visualization.

Eugenia Gerrard devised an ingenious way of sharpening our ability to visualize. We were attempting to meditate on people who were not in the group one day, and several members said they couldn't get any image. Eugenia said, "Everyone look at another person. Then close your eyes and see that person in your mind's eye."

## CAMERA EXERCISE

You can do this with a friend or with your own image in the mirror. First relax; close your eyes and breathe deeply. Open your eyes briefly, look at your friend or your image as if you were a camera taking a picture, then close your eyes. With your eyes still closed remember what you saw. If the image fades, open and close your eyes to take another picture. Do this at least ten times and see if the image lasts longer. You can practice this many times a day with objects, views and people. Have someone lead you to an object with your eyes closed, then let your eyes open like a camera's shutter to record the object.

Visualization is a skill that requires practice. Remember how long it took to learn your multiplication tables? The only way most of us acquire mental skills is through practice, and we are better equipped for this as adults than we were as children.

As we practiced we began to remember more. Eventually we could go home and lie in bed at night picturing every person in the group. It became a kind of camaraderie, because each of us had the group with us at all times. We learned it was easier to visualize others than ourselves, so we began looking in the mirror.

## MIRROR EXERCISE

1. With your eyes closed take long, slow abdominal breaths until you are pleasantly relaxed. Stand or sit in front of a mirror. Close your eyes for a count of ten. Open your eyes and take in your reflection without thought, judgment or intention.

2. Look for a minute or two, then close your eyes. When you lose the image, open your eyes and look in the mirror again. Repeat the exercise ten to twenty times.

If you resist this exercise at first don't judge yourself harshly. We have so many strong beliefs about the way we look and the way we would like to look. As we see ourselves our subterranean thoughts and feelings keep us from just *experiencing* the image. But after practicing this exercise a number of times you will be able to see your face. You will be able to see it in your mind's eye. And you will be able to look at yourself impartially, as a stranger might. Sometimes it can be a profound meeting.

One member of the group did, indeed, see a fundamental truth about herself in the mirror. ''I was horrified at what I saw looking back at me. I thought that if the people who loved me had forgiven all this, there must be some good in it after all. I looked for a long time into my eyes, and then I began to weep. I wept excessively for almost two hours—wept away a score of griefs—until I began to feel as if I were starting my life all over again.''

Another member of the group, a woman who had been extremely ill earlier in the year, said, ''I realized that all these years I never saw myself. I never wanted to look. It was like seeing somebody I knew very well but had never seen before.''

One way to use your powers of visualization is to maintain contact with people in your mind. For instance, we decided to visualize each other when we woke at night to see whether this influenced our dreams, and whether any members of the group felt the contact. We kept in mind where each person had sat on the day we did our visualization of the whole group.

For the next two weeks we each kept the group in mind at night. When we awakened, we would immediately survey the group in our mind's eye. Sometimes one person would stand out, sometimes another. It was a comforting experience. In the middle of the darkness the group was present, companionable. We knew the others were thinking of us. At our next meeting we wondered if we had influenced each other's dreams. Several people had dreamed of each other, but we couldn't find any direct evidence that we had been making a major impact on one another's dreams.

The visualization had accomplished two important things,

however: It had given us a way to feel together when we were apart, and had encouraged us to practice until we realized that we could, indeed, visualize.

At this point we decided to concentrate on one group member who was ill. We had no thought of any occult power of healing, but we knew there was psychological comfort for her in knowing we were all with her. She had been ill frequently during the year, had had pain from a hernia, and clearly it bothered her more than she admitted. She was reluctant to talk about it in the group and unfortunately we did not press her. She was a beautiful and independent person with a highly resonant sense of humor and adventure. If we asked about her health she was likely to divert us by describing the beauty of a visiting blue jay on her window sill. What happened to her is worth repeating, for it probably happens often to people in their 70s.

She had some internal bleeding, but initial tests were inconclusive. She began to have pain and it was assumed it was caused by her hernia. She was privately alarmed, but when her doctors did not push her to go into the hospital for further tests, she did not pursue the issue. This went on for months. Had she been younger it seems unlikely the doctors would have allowed her to go on so long without a clearer diagnosis. Only when the symptoms became really severe did she go back for testing, and she was told she must have surgery at once; there was a sizable tumor in her intestine that had not been detected before.

A few days before her operation she told us briefly what had happened. Then we realized that self-healing and taking responsibility for one's own health could be double-edged. Somehow we had persuaded her that she should and could heal herself, and she had been practicing visualization all year. Moreover we had not created sufficient trust or encouragement for her to voice her real feelings, to share with us what she must have considered a negative burden. She had been so engrossed in taking a positive direction that she had suppressed part of herself—as we were to see in the next two days. In spite of her courageous outlook and cheer she clearly had feelings of fear and anger. Two members of the group became "family," insisting on staying with her in the hospital until she went under anesthesia and again from the moment she regained consciousness until she felt better. At first she needed to vent her feelings. She was furious to learn she had cancer when she had been treated so casually for a hernia. Yet she had been afraid to find out, suspecting that something was terribly wrong.

Just before the surgery she felt defenseless and frightened. A friend of hers had recently died of cancer, and she wondered whether she would survive. When her feelings were drawn out she was able to cry, to talk, to clear her mind. By the time she was preparing for the anesthesia her mind was still and she was focused on healing.

As she began to come out of the anesthesia sheer physical pain hit her and she complained loudly, "Can't you get me someting to kill the pain? Can't you see I'm an old lady and I can't stand this!" For 24 hours she complained loudly. Nobody had ever seen that side of her personality.

We began to wonder whether we had unwittingly driven our friend to hide herself with our strong statements about positive attitudes. We had never intended to drive negative feelings underground, yet we had forgotten how hard it is to shake off the training to be nice. Another woman in the group was plainspoken and ill-tempered, and some participants would become uncomfortable and edgy when she insisted on her opinions or complained about her life. Women even more than men had been conditioned to deny negative feelings; to deny anger even to the point of feeling suicidal. All of us had colluded, and no matter what we said about being open and uncensored, we, too, had been hesitant to be complainers in the group. We had talked *about* our anger; we had expressed sorrow, fear and grief. But we had not been completely straightforward.

It is worth belaboring this point because there is energy and power in expression. Negativity is real. It will not go away just because we hide it, nor will its effects. Even subtle negative thoughts infest our bodies, and the people around us. Only by bringing them out into the light and examining our actions can we see what we do.

In this case, if our ill friend had complained about her pains early in the year, we might have urged her to push for diagnosis. She could have had an early warning that the symptoms were serious, and if she needed support to face the diagnosis, the group would have been with her.

## THE POWER OF ASSERTIVENESS

Selfishness has a survival value; less energy is wasted on pretending niceness and displaying false emotions. It is interesting to hear about the survival of cancer patients in treatment with Dr. O. Carl Simonton. Simonton was well known for his use of visualization and meditation techniques in concert with ordinary medicine. In looking at those of his patients who survived and those who didn't, he discovered that the survivors were not the pleasant, polite, compliant people, but the complainers—the selfish, assertive, "unlikable" people who were simply themselves.

The emergence of a negative streak in a very radiant person was instructive. After the first day's stress the terrible pain abated, and the woman rested. She began to act again as we had known her. She was visualizing a deep magenta that seemed healing to her, and letting it spread through her body, especially onto the painful incision. It hovered there like a mist of color. She could feel that it was healing. During much of the day she listened to tapes that allowed her to go into a light trance. As she described it later, she hovered over her body rather than feeling submerged within it.

Her visualization was simple. She would relax, inhale the healing color, see it pervade her body and help the wounded area. When she exhaled, she exhaled toxins and wastes from her system and visualized the healing magenta as muddier, or fainter, or a different color altogether as it left her body.

Sometimes as she did this one of us would sit with her, holding one hand about 12 inches above the incision while focusing energy at her. She said it felt very warm.

She spent most of her waking hours in visualization or meditation and doing foot movements and breathing exercises her doctor gave her. Visitors were limited. The surgeon had been surprised at the size of the tumor and was expecting a slow recovery. After the first three days, however, he saw something astonishing take place. His patient began feeling stronger, looking pink, getting restless. She wanted to walk around, despite the intravenous tubes. She was doing exercises in bed and visualizing healing much of the time. Only four days after surgery she was comforting another woman on her floor who also had cancer. Then her doctors asked her to talk to yet another patient before surgery.

Mexican and European hospitals often have space in each patient's room for family to stay and nurture the sick. Unfortunately this practice is uncommon in our efficient American hospitals. Except recently in a few progressive children's and maternity hospitals, we make no provision for feelings—for fear, anxiety, strangeness or anger—and their role in tension and disease. It seems as though we expect the ill and wounded to heal without love and relaxation. When we insisted on staying with our friend, it ran against all hospital conventions. Doctors and nurses objected vehemently, but finally gave in and placed a cot in her room. As the first few days unfolded, staff people began peeking in to see what was going on. A nurse who had learned psychic healing understood. Others were curious. They could see that it was doing no harm. Perhaps the attention, the affection and the meditations were actually helping. Attracted by this woman's grace and strong personality, one nurse insisted she be assigned to her and was dumbfounded by her progress. Throughout their shifts nurses would stop by to ask what she was doing, what tapes she listened to and what mental processes she practiced. They never expected to see a woman in her mid-70s snap back so rapidly from so serious a condition.

The color returned to her cheeks, the brilliance to her eyes, in four days. It was too fast, however. She had been comforting other patients and entertaining family and friends. One day as she walked around she began to have chest pains. There was adhesion, and fear of an embolism. Once again she lay flat on her back. This time she was told not to move at all. Lying still was a reminder to her of her fragility. When she went home a week later, she accepted that the recuperation process would take a lot of energy and that she would have to cut back on her activity for some time.

Soon another woman in the group needed similar surgery. This time the group was actively behind her. One person lent her tapes from Simonton. Several others met with her four days before her operation; all had used visualization methods themselves to get through illness or surgery. They began by helping her release her tensions. She had not admitted how angry she was at her doctors because they had diagnosed diverticulitis and only later found that it was cancer.

"I didn't realize how furious I've been." Not only had her doctors at first failed to make a correct diagnosis, but she felt they treated her in an insulting way. The radiation therapist was gruff and brushed her aside like a child when she asked to see the x-rays. When she inquired about nutrition she was ignored. But she had not blown up and told her doctors how angry she was; she had simply put it inside—smoldering.

## DEMANDING YOUR RIGHTS

What would you do? Many of us have had these feelings, but we were brought up to respect doctors and not to assert ourselves. Hospitals and medical centers expect compliance and cooperation. Yet if you are the patient, your *life* is at stake. Perhaps you are exhausted or frightened. You need a positive state of mind to heal. You need an ally, an advocate willing to probe and question relentlessly as long as some strong feeling has not been expressed.

"What are you most worried about that you're not saying?" Silence.

"In your shoes, I'd be worried about not surviving."

If you cannot unburden yourself of such fears and misery, meditation methods won't have much power. For most of us it is a matter of pride not to behave like a child, not to vent our emotions and scream, cry or complain. But once you have really let it go you can relax more fully. Only after the fury and the fears have been shared can people begin to use visualization.

A member of our group suggested: "Imagine a strongbox—of any size and description you like—with a lid that locks. Now picture yourself putting all your anxiety, worry, anger, concerns about family and other things in that box. Lock the lid securely. Leave all those problems for later."

When the patient had done this, her friend led her in an exercise for deep relaxation. She had been practicing, so this was easy and went fast.

"Now that you are deeply relaxed, see yourself as I see you. You are recovering rapidly. You are becoming vibrant and healthy. I see you coming back from the hospital and telling us in the community about your experience."

Up to the moment when she was rolled into the operating theater, friends worked with her. They asked the nurses to give them some time alone so she could be mentally prepared. "We're her friends and we think we can help her relax and heal better by using meditation."

"We all know about that here," one nurse said. "Two years ago there was another woman up here who did that. We all remember her."

A few days later, back in her room, the woman was emerging from the worst discomfort. She continued to visualize. She was an artist and had a unique way of seeing. She often evoked scenes from her youth, mountain peaks with cool breezes coming off the snow, fields of pale pink-gray flowers in the wind. Her doctor was surprised at her quick recovery. He had told her there were many things that could go wrong with someone as old as she was.

Doctor's attitudes can be a real problem, especially for older patients. Very often there is a tacit belief that the older patient will recover slowly or will have complications. But you can help yourself fend off such negativity.

You can be assertive and open. If you think your doctor's attitudes are negative, say so. Draw him or her out. Decide whether you want to entrust yourself to this person.

If you are preparing for surgery or hospitalization try to find someone who can give you emotional support during the experience. Your meditation and visualizations will be more effective with this kind of backup. Most of us need at least one reliable advocate when we have undergone trauma, especially if we are in a hospital.

## PREPARING FOR HEALING

1. Find friends or relatives who can share your attitudes and let them know how you feel and what you have learned. Do this now, while you are well. If you are doing exercises from this book or others, share them.

2. Choose an ally who is willing to let you release your feelings and who will help you.

3. Ask your ally to help you assert your needs to the hospital staff.

4. Ask your ally to stay with you to give you moral support,

massage if that is appropriate, and to run errands. If you want someone to stay with you overnight, arrange it. If you really insist, a hospital will sometimes put a cot in your room.

5. Ask your ally to guide you in your healing visualizations and meditations, and to sit with you and share them.

6. You may want to ask your ally to protect you from other friends and family in the first days after surgery or serious illness, since at that time a patient usually does not have the energy to respond to family emotions, to chitchat, or to put up with distractions.

When we visit a sick person we can easily drain him or her. We are worried about the person and caught up in our feelings. Sometimes we act out of habit, consoling, moaning, fussing ineffectually. Or, because nobody visiting a hospital or sickroom is without some anxiety, we try to amuse the patient, lighten his or her spirits with jokes, books, gossip, presents, news—all with the best of intentions. But in early stages of recovery the patient can be better helped by your own calm and peace. If need be, stop before entering his or her room and breathe for a while until you feel relaxed and centered. Then you can sit with the patient, perhaps giving him or her your own serene energy.

You might help the patient do a simple self-healing exercise such as the one that follows. Of course it is more effective if it has first been practiced in health. Many people say they could not have been so successful in healing themselves if they hadn't practiced relaxation and meditation for months beforehand.

## BREATHING-THROUGH-THE-SKIN EXERCISE

1. Find time when you will not be interrupted. Sit comfortably or lie down with a pillow under your knees. Be sure you are not wearing anything tight.

2. Close your eyes and breathe deeply. As you exhale, let all your worries, thoughts, concerns and previous feelings float away.

3. Visualize yourself—your entire body.

4. As you inhale, see or feel your entire body fill with radiant light. As you exhale feel or see all the toxins leaving your body through your breath and through the pores of your skin.

5. Breathe in, bringing the radiant light through your pores and feeling your body fill with it. See your exhalation carry any wastes out.

It is particularly effective if both patient and ally have practiced the same visualization, because when we are in pain it is helpful to have someone guide us. In a crisis we often forget to use the very methods we've learned unless someone else is there who can do them with us.

Why spend so much effort on mental healing? Eventually we all die; why prepare for surgery or illness years in advance?

Of course we cannot undo the path of nature. All we can do is improve the quality of our experience. Most of us have grown up learning that sickness is woe, a hospital experience stressful. Our culture conspires to make it that way. But we still have some control because we can alter our minds. By focusing on a color instead of on pain we can transform some of the energy into positive feeling. By reining in our anxiety when we visit people in a hospital or sickroom we can remain centered, make real contact, and leave without having exhausted them. Pain and sickness are not enjoyable, but with effort they are much less terrible than we expect.

This was particularly clear one dark evening when a colleague and friend miscarried and went to the emergency room for a dilation and curettage. Her husband and a friend acted as advocates. One doctor on duty scared her into thinking she might bleed to death if she didn't have an immediate operation. There were a few minutes of panic. Her husband said, "Wait a minute. I want to consult another doctor." At first he encountered resistance everywhere. He was going against policy. After a few phone calls he found a doctor who was willing to explain the procedure and do it without any drugs. "It's very simple," he said, "takes about 12 minutes. I use a vacuum."

After a brief discussion he agreed to do the operation with the husband and friend present. They asked the nurses to turn off the bright lights in the operating room until the doctor arrived. The friend and husband positioned themselves on either side of the operating table. Each took one of her hands, and they began a rhythm of slow breathing. When the doctor was ready the lights were turned up, and he began to say at each step what he would do. "Breathe in and hold it, and breathe out." The woman's face remained completely relaxed. She had no sedatives, no anesthesia. When the doctor was finished, everyone looked at each other with pleasure. No one was tired. There had been no stress. The nurses were elated.

Ten minutes later my friend was ready to go out to dinner. Contrast this with the ordeal many people make of a dilation and curettage. Or an appendectomy. Or almost everything. We do have options, but we do need each other to put them into action.

# CHAPTER 11

# DEATH AND DYING

For several days people called our office to ask for Joe, one of our central staff members. He was a healthy person who had been jogging for 10 years, who meditated and was an inspiration to many of us. We weren't overly concerned about his absence until he didn't appear for a meeting. All day his associates tried to stifle their anxiety. Then anxiety turned to alarm. After checking the hospitals, one person called the morgue. Joe had been found dead near the track where he ran six miles a day. He had a blissful smile on his face.

Our shock was profound. He was one of us. He was only 57. We depended on him. We fought with him. We loved and admired him. He was a deep spiritual seeker who had been exploring his feelings about death in order to help dying people; he had been preparing for two years. He was ready.

We were not. Once again we were confronted by the preciousness of our time together and the fragile, paper-thin quality of our lives. We lived under an illusion of control. But we did not control death or the larger purposes of which we felt a part.

Joe's family flew in from many parts of the country. They wanted us to perform the memorial service. This, they said, was his spiritual family and the home he had been seeking earlier in life. A retired Unitarian minister and staff member led an unforgettable service in a large meeting room at the hotel where we had our offices. Concentric semicircles of about a hundred chairs had been arranged around a large table with a bowl of flowers, a few of Joe's favorite objects, a large shell, and a picture of Christ. This service was at once subtle and very powerful.

We stood, holding hands and exploring our feelings for Joe. We did the most central part of all our breathing exercises, something we had done together hundreds of times. The minister instructed us to begin paying attention to our breathing. We could feel the pulsing of our hearts, the rhythm of breath all in the room shared. We were alive. Joe, who had led similar breathing exercises so many times with us, was no longer breathing. This unspoken distinction between life and death was a statement. The breathing released our feelings. Some of us wept.

Our farewell to Joe and celebration of his life with us had some of the qualities of our work together and expressed what our group was about. Standing and touching, as we had so often, we sang some of Joe's favorite songs and did a meditation for speeding his spirit to the light. It allowed our love for him to empower him and us. Gil, Joe's closest friend, had spent hours with Joe's family and had culled a biography of his early life, his career and lifelong spiritual quest. It was full of unfamiliar facts about a time when we hadn't known him. As members of his family spoke we began to know him better and learn how we fit in his life. They offered memories of this gentle yet passionate man and read from his favorite books. Then people began remembering him aloud, sometimes recalling fights or funny situations, and everyone laughed. There was no eulogy. We simply talked and shared our feelings.

One woman went up to a member of Joe's family when the service was over and said, ''Joe and I never got along. We fought like cats and dogs.'' This service did not force anyone to pretend that things were perfect. Another woman said she and Joe had finished their business and she was ready for the relationship to be over. There was no right or wrong thing to say. No reason to feel self-conscious. Men and women both felt free to weep openly. Afterward many of us had lunch with Joe's family. We had a real sense of communion, having shared our feelings very fully. This experience is not so common today as it was when communities were small and families larger. It was the kind of service I would like, would want to have at times of loss. It gave us support and intimacy and pulled our community together in a way that was strengthening.

Some of us wanted to see Joe's body, so we went to the mortuary. Many people in the community thought it barbaric: ''I don't want my body to be seen after I die,'' said one woman. ''I don't like what they do to you in the mortuary.''

It was true that Joe's beatific death smile had been changed. Without seeing his body, however, I could not have believed he was really dead. He had been an important person to me, the sharer of a vision and a moral support. I was not ready to let him go. Seeing him I had to acknowledge that he was indeed dead and I was alive. I had not seen my father's body after he died and there had been no shared mourning, no expression of feelings at the service. For years I was haunted by the unfinished relationship, by the feeling that my father was simply on a long trip and would one day return. Barbaric or not I felt it was important for me to see the body. Eugenia Gerrard said, ''I remember going to the hospital after my mother died. I had to see her body. I looked at her. It was her body, but it wasn't she. I felt as I had when my daughter was born and I examined her toes and her fingers and all of her. I was awed at what life was. By acknowledging that my mother was really dead I was affirming life, too. I was alive.''

Eugenia had nudged and prodded us into removing the veils of taboo and exploring our feelings about dying and death. We spent hours learning how to grieve, how to allow and support mourning, how to acknowledge loss, to face dying and death. So many of us had been sheltered from the basic facts of life. We were born in hospitals and had been prevented from seeing, touching, smelling and absorbing the fundamental conditions of life. What we were doing together was no more than countering our culture's deadening avoidance. The service we held for Joe, the openness of our feelings and support for one another, could not have happened except as the culmination of several years of continual work together. We had to use each crisis and death as a time to learn about our own emotions and beliefs.

We would never have pursued our feelings with such intensity and persistence except for Eugenia. She and I started the exploration out of our needs to deal with dying. My father had recently died, and her mother was dying.

Eugenia's mother had progressively receded into helplessness. She lay in bed unable to care for herself, to speak, even to understand. She was not old. She suffered from a brain disease. Eugenia, despite all the difficulties of moving and caring for someone in her mother's condition, brought her from Texas to California. She wanted to be near her before she died. It was an extemely stressful time for her, visiting her mother, touching her, talking to her, hoping and losing hope. Not many weeks before she died she was taken to the hospital in critical condition in need of oxygen. There she momentarily regained her ability to recognize the family and to speak. Then she relapsed and died. "I wouldn't have missed that chance to be with her as she was dying, not for anything. Life is so fleeting. I valued the chance to make real contact with her."

Eugenia's experience freed and inspired many people who might have passed up the opportunity to be with a dying parent or friend, who might have found it inconvenient to travel a long way, who were uncertain about interrupting their lives with a long dying process. As she pointed out, this transition can never be repeated. "I had learned everything from my mother—how to walk and talk, to dress, how to become a woman, how to live. This was my one chance to learn from her how to die. Death tells us to treasure the time we have because we never know when it will end, and we cannot control the time we will die. To run away from dying, or dying people, is to avoid acknowledging how precious life is. That time and that person can never be brought back."

## EXPLORING GRIEF

It's hard for many of us to express grief. We are well trained to suppress our deepest feelings, even when we know it is time to release them. Our group spent months exploring our emotions and learning to share feelings without self-consciousness. We cultivated our closeness and kept repeating to one another that it was okay to be human. It was several years before we could experience together the kind of community we felt in our memorial for Joe, and the freedom we had to be ourselves. It had taken several years of consciously creating intimacy and deliberately confronting the topics of dying and of death.

A year earlier another friend had died, a woman in her 70s whom we had grown to love. We were not yet a community then. Rose was the first. We all knew it would happen with someone, and that we were spending a great deal of time and conscious effort coming to know and love each other, only to lose each other one day. But when it happened we were not ready to share our feelings.

As we sat in our afternoon group to which Rose would never return, we mourned her. Many people were cool, casual. They said they no longer allowed themselves to feel too strongly. They had lost too many people. Grief took too much out of them. That seems to be what we tell ourselves: that we will save energy if we do not express grief. Yet that afternoon the tension and fatigue in the room suggested that the unexpressed feelings were still strong and present.

## IMAGE EXERCISE

On the spur of the moment Eugenia invented an exercise to unseal those feelings—an exercise you can adapt for yourself. "Close your eyes," she instructed us, "and see Rose in your mind's eye. When you have an image of her, find out what part of yourself she represents."

"I see a young girl, just emerging."

"I see someone dependent and clinging."

"I see a power and artistic talent just starting."

"I see my trapped self."

"I see an immensely caring woman."

We placed an empty chair in our circle for her. Eugenia asked one of the men to leave the circle and sit elsewhere in the room.

"Now let's do the same thing with Herb."

An empty chair was left for him, and the group began to express their feelings about him, what he represented to each person.

"Now remove Gay."

As each person left the group the circle became smaller. Suddenly people began to weep. They were losing parts of themselves with each person who left the group: At some point it became too evident to deny any longer.

That was an important session for us, not only because we discovered what parts of ourselves we lost in the loss of each other, but because we saw a way of bringing these feelings to the surface. We would never have expressed how much we cared for each other, how much it meant to have each other present. Often we take each other for granted. We act calm about an illness and stoical about a death. We let our feelings remain dormant. Perhaps this is the importance of uninhibited mourning: It allows us to recognize our own deep feelings.

Most of the time, instead of using an exercise to bring our emotions to the surface we do the opposite. Rather than permit ourselves to face the full meaning of a threat or loss at the time it happens, we repress the feeling, stay numb. That means we don't admit the full meaning of the people we care about, either to ourselves or to them. These unspent feelings seem to stay with us in strange ways. For instance, there were people who were still mourning loved ones who had died 20 or even 60 years earlier. They had not been able to deal with the feelings at the time, and they were still unable to shake the traumatic effects. Once feelings are released, you usually feel energy. Emotion is, indeed, the motion of a feeling expressed, carried outward. If the motion of our feelings is stopped, we use our energy to hold them back. But if we allow ourselves to share the feelings we were forbidden to express in our families, the taboo subjects become bearable.

## REVEALING OUR HIDDEN FEELINGS

Sex and death are two topics of conversation during which nobody's mind wanders. People don't sit and pick at their nails or rearrange their clothing or look out the window. Nobody can be neutral or uninvolved with those subjects. If a person plays cool, he or she is likely trying not to have feelings. But ultimately we cannot escape them: Our bodies know them. The deep recesses of our minds are crammed with them. They are part of us. No way can we escape. Our best alternative is to bring them to the surface and use them.

If our feelings of loss are hidden and our fears about dying are suppressed, we may not be able to act upon the things that have real meaning to us because we will not yet know ourselves. We all know the extent to which the topics of death and dying have, until recently, been socially taboo—things to be feared and avoided. The avoidance has even extended to the elderly and the dying. At the very time in their lives when people may need help and support the most, we avoid confronting their real needs. How many elderly people in institutions live polite, apathetic, isolated lives, already counted out? Sometimes they are dismissed as ''senile,'' which is another way of saying nobody wants to find out what they are actually experiencing. Perhaps they are in transition, finishing up with unfinished feelings and life events. In a nursing home we discovered that people who were thought to be demented were leading intense inner lives. One woman who had been brutalized when she was young was sitting on unexpressed rage. Another woman who was supposedly completely disoriented was communing with her dead husband in preparation for death.

Not only are dying people avoided. In many institutions if a roommate dies in the middle of the night the body is taken away silently. No word is said by the staff, no feelings are expressed. Is it any wonder so many people sit and stare out the window, or at a television set, or at the wall? The most important transition, ending life, is overlooked and nobody is encouraged to feel or speak about it. What is left? By overlooking death, we diminish the value of life.

We all have strong feelings about dying ourselves, and about the deaths of people we love, but how many of us talk about them, share with others our fascinations and fears? It would change our lives and our relationships with one another if we could admit our feelings.

Whenever people begin to tell their children or grandchildren how they think they are going to die, the family says, "Oh, Gram, you won't die"—which is ridiculous. If somebody is in the hospital, sick, you never say, "You might die." You say, "You'll be well. Everything will work out."

That is what my father said the night before he died. One of the few things I regret is my part in allowing him to die in isolation. None of us could bear to acknowledge that he was dying; we kept wishing he would get better, acting cheerful, talking about his future. Although he knew we loved him we would not allow him to talk about dying, and by maintaining our longed-for deception we deprived him of real contact. Despite his dazed look he knew where he was. He was in a hospital dying, and his family was acting as if he weren't, and all of us were suffering underneath. Had we all been honest, we would have shared those last weeks and had a feeling of real closure and closeness.

Surely we could not fool him about our real feelings. Nothing can be kept secret. Feelings, however hidden, are vibrations of energy that broadcast themselves to the world and people around us at all times. Our most private thoughts, even if they are not conscious, are known. Thus if we love someone, he or she knows it without our words. If we are angry, or dislike someone, the person knows that, too. We may not be aware of our own feelings, but we transmit them.

Grief is an inevitable part of life, unavoidable, yet many of us have been taught to hold back our feelings and not admit their intensity, as if we could avoid pain by not expressing it. But we also thus prevent ourselves from experiencing important release, a letting go that is the essence of vitality and rebirth.

## TIME FOR GRIEF

Think. If there is a death that has gone unfinished in your life, or a loved one who's dying, find someone you can really talk to and tell him or her what you feel.

People often act stoically and don't recognize their feelings. One 80-year-old woman, preparing for an operation, said, "Well, I've got everything ready. My husband was a doctor, and I burned all his records. I have updated my will stating who's to get everything.''

''So you're ready to go?'' There was a long pause, as if I wasn't supposed to ask that. Then she said, ''Is anybody ever ready?''

That is probably what most people say. Who among us is ready? What does it take to be ready? One way of exploring that question for ourselves in groups was to find out what felt unfinished in our lives. The exercise we did was extremely simple. You can do it for yourself by taking pen and paper, and a little time for reflection.

## ARE-YOU-READY-TO-DIE EXERCISE

1. Sit comfortably.
2. Take some time to relax with your eyes closed.
3. If you died tomorrow, what would you leave undone? Write out all the things you can think of. It might be Who would take care of my cat? What about my unpaid bills? What about my sick daughter? Or you may have other concerns: My ex-wife and I are still angry; it doesn't feel finished. I don't want to die until I regain my faith in God. I don't have faith in anything. I'm not ready. Or it may be unfinished communications: I never told my son I love him—or why I have no money to leave. I know my daughter is just waiting to be rid of me—but I've never said it.

If you have a sense of ''not ready,'' perhaps you will want to get comfortable and close your eyes. See if anything pops into your mind. Is there anyone you sense holds a grudge against you? Is there anyone you have a grudge against? Anyone you need to ask forgiveness of? Or forgive? The universe is so interconnected that you can accomplish this by doing it in your own heart. You may want to place your hand gently and lightly over the center of your chest, and feel yourself very lightly embracing in your heart a person you need to forgive for something. Similarly, open your heart, imagining yourself with someone to whom you feel you owe an apology, or whose forgiveness you must ask. In any case make your peace with love. You will feel lighter and happier.

When you imagine dying, what are some of the things you worry about? People commonly say they do not want to be a burden to someone else. They do not want to suffer, to become helpless or demented. Some people fear pain. Others fear losing control of their lives. What are your concerns?

Write your obituary. It should be a long article about who you were and what you did with your life. Do you think the writer would label you a good person or bad, someone who helped others or didn't? What idiosyncracies, tastes, adventures, family, profession would the writer describe? What kind of character and personality was this person who was you?

See if there is someone in your life with whom you can share these things.

Dying and growth have much in common. Whether it is letting go of a mother's hand, ending bachelorhood to be married, having a first baby, saying goodbye to a dying parent—or dying oneself—the process is similar. And each of us will do it in our own way.

Letting go. It means relinquishing the habits and feelings, the behaviors that kept you ''feeling like yourself.'' It means letting go of one role in order to proceed to another phase of your life. The way you typically have ended the various stages of your life is likely to be the way you will die.

## TAILOR YOUR DYING TO YOURSELF

When we talk about readiness to die, most of us act as if dying were not a part of our lives.

How do you want to die? Do you want to be conscious and aware? Do you want to be snuffed out quickly?

Close your eyes and see yourself dying.

When asked this question, we gave different answers.

"I want to die alone, quietly."

"I'm going to die in my sleep."

"I want to die suddenly. To never know what happened."

"I'm going to die with my family around me. I'll tell them what I'm seeing."

"I want to die by myself, slowly, but not so I'd be a burden on anyone."

"I want to die in a garden in the late afternoon in the sunlight. I want to be held by someone I love and trust."

"I want to be held by someone, but I don't want that person interrupting me and asking a lot of questions."

Some people said they didn't care exactly how they died, just so they didn't suffer from a lingering, burdensome illness.

1. Take some deep breaths. Relax completely. Close your eyes.

2. As if you were watching a movie, watch the way you want to die. Where are you? Who do you want to have with you? What are you doing?

Sometimes a bizarre scene will pop into mind. Just watch it. It does not mean things will happen that way. It only means that this is what you see right now.

As we did this exercise one day, tears were streaming down the face of one man. He had seen himself in a meadow with his wife and one of his sons and he had never known how much they loved him.

Another man said he had left his body in half sleep.

For many of us, these exercises were only a preamble to self-discovery. We had managed to repress our deepest fears so successfully that we could manage imaginary situations and deal with them. We needed to probe our feelings more deeply.

Eugenia Gerrard trained many nurses, social workers and other professionals who worked in convalescent hospitals or nursing homes. She said, "One thing I feel very strongly is that you can't deal with people who are dying until you have dealt with your own feelings about dying."

The following exercises will help you get in touch with your own feelings about dying. They were adapted from Stanley Keleman's book, *Living Your Dying*. They are good exercises to do with somebody you trust. If there is no one to share them with, write down your observations about yourself.

## ENDINGS AND TRANSITIONS

1. Make sure you will not be interrupted for at least an hour. Remove constricting clothing, jewelry, contact lenses, glasses. Sit comfortably in a chair and close your eyes.

2. You are going to take a trip backwards in time to the first

days you left your family to go to school. Try to remember as much as you can. You will need to begin reliving that experience. Try to remember the first day of school—or one of the first days. Stand up. Keep your eyes closed and imagine you are entering that class as a small child. Get an image of the room and the day. You are tiny. You may not think you remember, but feel your body. Express what you were feeling with your body. Were you fearful, hanging onto your mother or sibling? Were you crying? Were you angry and defiant? Were you brave? Did you get sick? Were you eager? Rebellious? Cooperative? Sneaky?

This was a major turning point in your life. It was your entrance into society, the entrance of society into your young world. You were suddenly subject to an authority other than your family. How did you handle it? Did you swallow your feelings and comply? Did you resist? What did you feel and what did you do?

This was the same authority as the doctor who says, "I'm not going to release you. You are going to stay here in the hospital." How did you handle that authority situation when you were young? How do you handle it now?

3. Write down your observations or share them with a partner. Each of us selects a pattern and lives with it, seeing that way of reacting as the only option. But in truth people handle turning points in their lives very differently. Some are crushed by change; others are challenged, excited, and grow.

4. Take a break of 15 or 20 minutes.

5. Relax, breathe deeply, and close your eyes. Go back in time.

6. Remember your very first sexual experience and how you handled it. You might have been six, or 12 or 16—it doesn't matter. You may have lived on a farm and seen animals copulating or birthing, or you may have been playing with friends and showing

each other your genitals. You may have read something or masturbated. Simply try to recall that first experience and feel in your body how you handled it. How did you handle the excitement? Did you go with it? Were you ashamed, proud, fearful? Did you feel pleasure, pain, satisfaction, furstration? Try to recall your body position during that first experience. What muscles tightened? Did you become forward and open? Did you become shy or adventuresome, aggressive or passive? Did you hold back, repressing your feelings and pretending they weren't there?

It doesn't matter what your pattern was. Just see whether you can recognize that pattern. Now see how it influenced your subsequent sex life.

Early sexual encounters are turning points. From the safe world of being neutral we emerge as sexual beings. There are many social proscriptions laid upon us. How we react to these is relevant to how we are going to die. Think about your pattern and write down your feelings and observations, unless you can share them directly with a partner or group.

7. Think about how you end things. How do you end relationships? How do you wind up a phase of your life? Think of important endings in your past. One might be the end of school and the beginning of worklife; another might be the end of single life and the beginning of marriage. How did you feel as you were deciding to get married, and just after you did? What happened to you after the birth of your first child? How did you say goodbye to someone close who left your life? How did you make a move, change jobs, decide to retire? Did you act suddenly or gradually? Did you resist the change until you had no choice? Did you express your feelings or deny them? Did you become emotional? Did you withdraw or share your feelings? See if you usually end things

in pretty much the same way, whether it be a romantic relationship, a friendship, a job, or a period of residence.

If you can see your pattern of endings, it offers you the possibility of changing—if you want to. Again, you will likely die the way you are carrying out your life.

Most of us live out of touch with our own brevity. If we always remembered that we are going to die, we might spend our time on Earth differently. We might take more risks to discover what does satisfy us in life. But for the most part we do not remember that we will die.

Children talk about their fear of dying. They ask frank questions about dead animals or relatives, and they often wonder what it would feel like to be dead. How often do you talk about it with your peers? Children ask what is on the other side. Is it terrifying? Will it hurt? Will anyone be there with me? Will I be able to fly? Will I see and hear? Will I come back as another baby? Will I remember? Are there ghosts?

When was the last time you asked these questions of anyone your own age?

It is too bad that we have all been given dogmatic answers in childhood, as if anyone really knew. "There is nothing after death." "There is an afterlife like this one in heaven." "There is reincarnation." "There is hell." "There is life with beings from other planets, and other forms." And so on. Dogmatic answers quickly stifle curiosity and our willingness to venture and find out. If someone in authority says to us at an early age, "All experience ends with death," there is nothing to expect or discover. We may take years to discover that there is something else, another way to live that we can unfold for ourselves. The same is true of dying. We can only understand how we feel about dying by trying to die a little bit. We must experience, without censoring, some foretaste of our own death.

## DEATH FEELINGS

Stanley Keleman's half-breath exercise offers an ingenious and profound way to uncover some of your deep feelings about dying.

1. Pick as a partner some friend or relative with whom you would like to die. In this exercise you will get in touch with real feelings about dying, fear, panic, excitement, letting go, the adventure of the unknown.

2. Sit comfortably.

3. Take a deep, long breath and exhale fully.

4. Close your eyes.

5. Take another deep, long breath, counting the seconds, and exhale.

6. Take a breath that gives you half as much air as you had last time, and exhale fully.

7. Take in half as much air as you did last time, and exhale.

8. Take more breaths, each half of the one before, until you are taking in no air at all. Pay close attention to your body feelings. Don't avoid them. Don't cheat! Really continue cutting your breath until you are out of oxygen. Then wait as long as you can, watching your feelings.

10. When you absolutely have to take a new breath, do so, watching your feelings carefully.

11. Share what you experienced: Write it down if you are alone.

Some people get too frightened to do this exercise correctly. Some avoid their feelings. Others are startled.

"I felt very aware that this was an exercise. I couldn't play-act my way into dying."

"I felt a palpitation in my gut that reminded me of crying deeply."

"I felt total panic."

"I was gasping. I felt I wanted to hang onto something. I was terrified. For a moment I thought I was really dying."

"I felt fear, at first. I got really cold. Then I felt like I went through a big wave. I gave up. I was floating. I suddenly felt wonderful. Images came to mind. I became almost ecstatic!"

"I got to a point where I no longer cared. I felt deeply relaxed. It felt pleasant."

"I felt like I was floating above my body, out of it, and I could have kept on going."

This exercise is graphic and to the point. Only the knowledge of how we act will allow us to change, if we want to.

As we die we are forced to let go of life. It is the process of letting go that most of us fear in dying. Surely we cannot vanish from this enormous universe. There is nowhere else to go. But we must change form. We cannot hold these molecules and these atoms together in the same form forever. Even the sun, the other stars, the galaxies change. Is it the change of form we fear?

## ADVENTURES IN DYING

If you had the choice of looking toward death as an adventure, a challenge, a pleasurable experience instead of a fearful one, what would you prefer? That is hardly a question. Most of us don't realize there are many possible ways to experience a life transition, in particular that of dying. In the early 1970s a young psychologist,

Dr. Charles Garfield, worked in a hospital studying attitudes. Some of the people he saw were dying, others were healthy.

He questioned them closely as to their feelings about death and dying. In brief his survey indicated that certain kinds of "mental" experience seemed to lead people toward a more positive feeling about dying. They had less fear and generally more positive attitudes. The experiences they had might be called transcendent or spiritual. Some of those interviewed had these peak experiences after taking psychedelic drugs such as LSD. Others had them during meditation. Both the meditators and the drug-takers showed less fear of death than most other people.

What was the nature of the experience that changed their veiw of dying? It is an experience we have heard about all our lives. It is in the Bible. And Saint Therese of Avila, one of the great Christian saints, along with many Christian mystics and many followers of other religions, have described an ecstatic feeling of unity with all the universe. Abraham Maslow in *The Farther Reaches of Human Nature*, William James in *Varieties of Religious Experience*, Swami Yogananda in *Autoboigraphy of a Yogi*, Richard Bucke and others in *Cosmic Consciousness*, and countless more have described a sudden total perception of reality, of its intense beauty; feelings of being dissolved as a separate entity, of being absorbed, accepted, lifted up into the entire world, into intense love; seeing matter dissolve into light; seeing all things become intertwined, in a diffused yet intense glory. The experience involves going beyond the usual confines of the little self, the little personality one must wear for a while, and becoming boundaryless, beginning to see beyond the boundaries, to feel part of the sea, stars, and all beings.

Often within this experience people mention that a sense of timelessness is important, that they no longer experience their lives as the small, short events in which they have been immersed. Instead they know they are part of an endless process. Always taking new form. Death is simply the ending that must take place before the next form can be shaped. This is not new. Probably no person alive has not had some kind of peak experience, often in childhood, often in the last moments of dying. These experiences bring the message that life is not limited to what we know about, nor to the infinitesimal timespan of a human life.

If we pay attention, we may live a double life. On the one hand we are immersed in family cares, petty problems, material things. But some part of us extends beyond this conditioned reality—some part of us that feels free, undifferentiated, spacious, light, interwoven with what is around us. These are feelings of deep assurance. They cannot be achieved by expecting them, for there is no way to coerce feeling, cosmic or otherwise. However, the route used by most of the peoples of Earth since life began here has been a process now known as meditation.

## CHAPTER 12

# MEDITATION AND
# MEDITATIVE EXERCISES

Somewhere, somehow we all have an inkling that the lives we lead, the languages we speak, the foods we eat, homes we live in, relationships we maintain are not the only ones, are not sacred, are not some absolute reality. They are merely small apertures through which we have seen a tiny portion of what life can be. Highly individuated, differentiated people, we suffer from isolation.

Our tribal brothers do not even know what that is. They do not know what it is to have desires or relationships not decreed by the tribe. They have no separate property or children. If we human beings can see the reality of life on Earth so differently, what slight perception must we have of reality as a whole! Here we are on this insignificant blue planet that is part of a tiny solar system on the edge of a galaxy that is but a quantum, a mere drop in the vastness of a sea made up of billions of galaxies.

That immensity is where we come from.

We all know deep inside that this immensity is our parent. But how can we contemplate such things when we are busy making a living or raising children? It seems quite right that great philosophers and teachers and religious leaders tend to mature at the end of their lives. It should be a time we all look forward to, a kind of promise. We have an intuition of something very great when we are children, but we have too little experience and skill then to find what we seek.

We spend our years acquiring external skills and maintaining material existences. Then what?

"I think it's very sad that homemakers who have brought up families and gone through crises, or businesspeople who have reached retirement, don't have any sense of self-worth. But we haven't been taught to think we're beautiful, and all of a sudden we come to the later years and we have neither faith in ourselves nor the courage to enjoy those years."

"The people who are admired are those who are 75 and still doing what they have done all their lives—the busy, active people."

"It's true, I've been feeling guilty about not shouldering responsibility for Christmas and Thanksgiving. Maybe it's an intuitive way of saying 55 years of that were enough!"

We asked ourselves why we couldn't slow down. Most of us felt some fear that if we stopped performing the rituals of our lives we would retrogress. Was it a fear of dying in some way? Or a fear of beginning a second life?

There are many reasons why we don't pursue our inner lives with the same emphasis we give externals. In part we need to quiet that external turmoil before there can be an inner life. It took a full year of practicing relaxation, group contemplation and other processes like guided visualization before the first members of our group began asking serious questions about meditation. They asked for lectures, books and instruction. And they often thought we were falsely humble or coy when we evaded such questions as "What is meditation?"

Meditation is a truly vast subject. We are extremely fortunate to be living now. Books on meditation abound. We can learn procedures and philosophies from all over the world. This was not so until the 1960s. Of course much of the nonindustrialized world has always practiced some kind of meditation. Usually it is slow and undramatic. Nonetheless the focused mind can unleash energies that lie dormant within the body in a way that may be analogous to the atomic power released by nuclear fission. An unprepared person might find this concept overwhelming. Partly because of this these disciplines were usually kept secret or esoteric and reserved for the spiritual initiate under the guidance of a teacher. Many of the exercises are available in books now—but there is no gain in endlessly reading about the inner focus and discipline even the most introductory exercises demand. Only by practice can we have such focus.

If you have been practicing a relaxation exercise from this book or others, you have been laying a foundation for the inner quiet you need.

One of the easiest ways to start is to do a walking meditation. This will restore your appreciation of the miracle you take for granted every time you take a step. Our appreciation is probably greatest when we are toddlers and have been working for hours to stand upright, then, finally, take a few steps. As adults we do not remember how many hours a day we worked and what effort it took to get out of our crawling posture and place our vulnerable selves upright—but that was a vital part of our development. Even as young children we quickly forgot that balance and vulnerability were important to us. We no longer felt what we were doing as we shifted our weight from foot to foot. Until we suffer from some physical impediment, we take walking quite for granted.

## SILENT-WALKING MEDITATION

You can do this alone, but it has additional power in a group. You need about 40 minutes free of distractions.

1. Find a level space. If you are walking inside a room, move furniture and small rugs so you have the longest possible unhindered walk. If you are in a group, find an outdoor space or a room that is 20 to 40 feet long.

2. Begin by standing in place. (In a group, all begin at once, standing in lines so that each person can walk the full distance.) Take a few deep breaths with your eyes closed. Then open your eyes and softly focus on the ground three or four feet ahead of you.

3. Begin shifting your weight from foot to foot. Just feel your balance shifting. Feel your feet on the ground. This is best done barefoot or in stocking feet.

4. Feel your center of gravity. You may imagine that you have a heavy lead ball inside your lower abdomen, which is the center of your balance and power.

5. Looking at the ground three to four feet ahead, begin to take a step. Do it as slowly as you possibly can. Walk as if the air around you were thick honey. If you lose your balance going so slowly, walk at the slowest speed you can manage.

6. As you begin to walk very slowly, pay attention to the way you are breathing. Pay attention to each tiny motion, to the feeling of your heels and toes on the ground, your ankles. Feel your calf and thigh muscles as you move. Feel your hips, your joints. You will become aware of the way your pelvis tilts, your spine moves, and the position of your head and shoulders. Feel your arms. When you walk every part of you is in motion. See if you can perceive by paying attention.

7. Periodically return to your breathing. Is it relaxed? If your mind wanders from the tiny motions of your slow walking, gently bring it back. If you do this correctly, it may take you half an hour to walk across a large room.

8. The longer you walk in silence, paying attention to each movement, the quieter you will feel when you finish.

We first did this one afternoon in a room that was only about 24 feet long. There were twelve of us. We took 10 minutes to cross the room. Several people said they needed to work on regaining their balance.

"I didn't realize my balance was so bad. I found that very hard, going slow, you know. I kept feeling as if I were going to fall over."

"I found it very peaceful. I was surprised. I felt so serene when we were done. I didn't know how long we had been going." Later this speaker added, "I walk about two miles a day. Now I do it with a different attitude, more like a meditation. It's very relaxing."

The effect of a large group moving together in slow motion can slow down your sense of the outside world. The vision of someone's heel lifting almost imperceptibly slowly off the gound and the toe following can give the impression that time has all but stopped and you are coming to a new dimension.

It is important to practice this exercise in a relaxed state, which becomes easier after you have done it a couple of times. Let your eyes be soft, your mouth hang open. If your eyes get tired it means you have not been relaxing them. As you become relaxed and sensitive, you will feel body sensations: These are normal, but usually you are too mentally noisy to hear them.

Guilt and trying too hard seem to be problems for most of us. We have grown up learning that what we achieve should be attained by effort. Yet in meditative exercises we cannot achieve anything by effort.

When you try, you may be trying to become something you aren't, to accomplish something outside yourself. All our lives most of us look for satisfaction and pleasure outside ourselves. We think movies, books, entertainments, sporting events or other people ought to provide our pleasure. We think we must create something, achieve something to be satisfied. Yet all of us have had the experience of being in a virtual paradise, perhaps on a holiday or vacation, and finding that we didn't enjoy it. Once I had that experience standing on a pier in an exquisite bay with seals cavorting all around me. I became very depressed. I thought I should be happy; that I could force myself to be happy if I just made the right effort.

Effort destroys. When you are tense and want to sleep, relaxation eludes you. You may need to bring some feelings to the surface and express them. You can do this by being very nice to yourself. Treat yourself like someone you are deeply in love with, someone very precious to you. If thoughts intrude, admit gently what you are thinking. Then you can draw your attention back to what you began to do. Don't get involved in your thoughts. Just feel your body. Feel your muscles, especially the muscles around your eyes. Feel them relaxing. Sense the pleasantness of that feeling. Don't pay too much attention to whether thoughts flit by or not.

Feeling satisfaction and quietude in ourselves takes practice. Perhaps you have already begun, sitting in some pleasant place, contemplating. As you do this repeatedly your mind will stop its chatter and memory, its interruption of your tranquillity. If you don't believe it is your own mind that prevents you from feeling serene, try the following exercise just once.

## COUNTING THOUGHTS AND FEELINGS

Make certain you will not be interrupted for 20 minutes by people, pets or phones.

1. Sit in a quiet place. Put a timer or alarm clock in the room and set it for 15 minutes.

2. Sit comfortably with your eyes closed and relaxed as you would during contemplation.

3. Every time you have a thought, feel a physical sensation, hear an outside sound or experience an image or fantasy, count it. Count every thought, sensation and image you experience during the 15 minutes.

The first time I did this I spent what I considered a quiet hour, relatively devoid of thoughts and chatter, yet counted 1,060 items. It is impressive to watch your own mind's activity. Without watching the monkey that is your mind, you have no idea what you are about to train in meditation.

One afternoon a remarkable yogi began to chant while people were lying on the floor to rest. He chanted, "Om Mani Padme Hum." It is a famous mantra of compassion, recited and chanted by Buddhists all over the world. Slowly, without moving, the group members began to join the chant. They chanted softly for half an hour. Everyone was moved, although nobody knew the meaning of the Sanskrit words. (Whole books have been written on the meaning of the mantra; you can read about it in Lama Govinda's works cited in the bibliography.)

As people sat up following the quiet chant, a lovely woman passed out flowers from her garden. Each person sat and simply looked at a flower. There was silence. Many people said later that they felt an unusual peace and beauty. Some people were already meditating. This was the kind of experience that helped prepare members to sit in silence and be relaxed enough to remain still and focused.

Meditation is an experience, not a concept, and it grows with practice. It is a way of being, a way of experiencing. Keep that in mind as you read about meditation in this book and others, for you can never read what *your* experience will be or will do for you.

## CONTEMPLATION

Set aside 15 minutes without interruption. Select something you would like to contemplate. It can be a vase, a piece of jewelry, a piece of bark from a tree, a flower, a leaf, a stone.

1. Sit comfortably with the object in your hand or nearby. Close your eyes and take five deep breaths, following your breath with your attention.

2. Open your eyes. Caress the object visually. Allow it to fill your vision and your entire attention. If you have other thoughts, bring your attention back to the object. Gently silence yourself and again caress the object with your eyes.

3. Start with one minute, then two, twice a day. Then spend at least 10 to 15 minutes twice a day. If you repeat this exercise twice a day for two weeks you will find that a new and lovely silence allows you to focus openly on your object of contemplation.

This is a good way to encourage your mind to "one-pointedness," which is an important skill.

You will discover, as you repeat this exercise, that there is a richness you may never have suspected in common objects, in fragments of natural objects, and in your communication with them. Some people seem to do this without being taught, but most of us need to practice.

Another way to prepare for meditation is to sit quietly, relaxing the body, quieting the mind as much as possible, and remaining aware. It is a process in which deep bodily and mental relaxation allows the usual thoughts to fade away and be replaced by concentration on a visualization. The visualization may be some external symbol, or some internal function such as sensing and counting one's own breaths.

If we said that meditation was quieting, nobody would be satisfied. Mere quieting hardly explains why meditation has such a powerful grip on millions of people. You will observe that one of the important aspects of meditation is a turning inward and understanding of yourself. You cannot get a look at your own nature, your character, the kinds of images and projections your mind persistently conjures up. At first this activity of the mind is an obstacle. It prevents quiet and focus. And most of us do not know how to watch it without becoming involved. Those are not just thoughts, they are *our* thoughts. Those images and memories are not just any images; they are our *life*. Yet after a while we can suspend our attachment to them and watch them as if they were in the mind of a stranger.

The first step is to remove ourselves from mental chatter. We are often conversing with ourselves, distracting ourselves with plans and prospects, anticipating what we will say or do or how we will feel. And if we are not busy anticipating the future, we are immersed in the past—in memories, longings and retrospects. This prevents us from being immersed in the richness of what is happening right now. What is happening as you read this sentence? You cannot read it if your mind is elsewhere. Yet you cannot force your mind to stop its commotion. You must patiently allow it to stop. The more stern your effort to stamp out your inner chatter, the more your mind will keep churning.

## QUIETING THE MIND

You can begin by taking an assigned time each day—whether it is five minutes or half an hour—to just sit without interruption.

1. Sit comfortably; remove glasses and loosen tight jewelry or clothing.
2. Take a few deep breaths with your eyes closed and your attention on your breathing.
3. Sit and watch whatever is behind your closed eyelids. If it seems like "nothing," watch the nothing. Your mind will grow more silent if you are kind to yourself. You cannot force it. If your attention wanders and you start to go off into a fantasy or thought, bring your attention back to watching what is behind your eyelids.

This simple discipline will slowly build your tolerance and ability. As you practice, however, you must stay with your moment-to-moment experience. It is important not to get stuck in feelings or sensations, not to grasp something in particular. The beginnings of a deep experience and knowledge are already in you.

Look at all things growing and flourishing. Also pay close attention to dead leaves withering, fading and dying. Observe these things. Feel them, but do not judge one better than another. Do the same with sounds; listen to a car engine, a bird, an airplane. Hear the sounds around you with detachment and without labels.

You can do the same thing when you listen to people. Listen silently without inner comment or judgment. If someone expresses an opinion with which you disagree or that makes you feel uncomfortable, don't stir. Practice listening with quietness.

Look at yourself with the same dispassion, but do not ignore your thoughts. They are as important in your being as tables and chairs are in your home.

You may want to look at the way you use your energy. How much do you expend in casual conversation? Talking takes energy, like anything else. How much energy do you spend in responding, being vexed, angry, fearful, emotional or contentious? For example, do you need to be right when you are in a debate? As you begin observing yourself, you are beginning an attitude of meditation.

At some level there is really no difference among prayer, meditation, invocation, and the kind of contemplative state in which some people naturally find themselves and in which they are able to come to a greater reality in their experience. But for most people self-recognition is a hard process. Most of us would like to throw away, avoid or neglect the negative aspects of ourselves, as though they were not part of the whole. Yet these are important to use and experience fully, to witness and transcend.

Long-repressed feelings and intensities can occur during meditation, and ideally you can handle them like unwieldy thoughts, seeing them, experiencing them, but not lingering with them.

Many people are not sufficiently aware and controlled for this detached observation of the painful parts of themselves. Some people find that a therapist or guide can be helpful in this process of self-recognition. After you have achieved some quiet, you may begin to be aware of the way your mind works, the way thoughts form, the way sensory images are interpreted.

## DEVOTION

Wherever there is the concept of an external, "higher" being, there is also an internal personality known as "I," or the ego. This often means you feel yourself to be inferior and are trying to contact something higher, greater. Such meditation practice becomes a way of developing communication with a higher being. It is based on devotion. Emphasis is placed on an inward state so that there is no awareness of one's own senses—only of God. One finds a similar technique in the orthodox teachings of Christianity where the prayer of the heart is used, and concentration on the heart is emphasized, as a means of identifying oneself with God. The basic belief is that one is separate from God, but one is also part of God. By using emotions and devotional practices aimed at making contact with God or gods or some particular saint, a unity is experienced. Devotional practices often include the recitation of mantras like "Om," or prayers.

## ACTIVE MEDITATION

Another form of meditation takes an almost opposite approach, but it can have the same results. There is no belief in a higher and lower. The idea of different levels, or of being in an underdeveloped state, does not arise. One does not feel inferior and what one is trying to achieve is not something higher than oneself.

This practice does not require an inward concentration on the heart; there is no centralizing concept at all. It is concerned with trying to see "the nature of existence." It is not, therefore, the result of some long-term arduous practice to attain a higher state, nor does it necessitate falling into any kind of inner trance state. This is what one might call working or extrovert meditation, where skillful means and wisdom must be combined like the wings of a bird. There is no question of trying to retreat from the world. Without the world, the meditation would be almost impossible to practice. The individual and the external world are not separate, but co-exist. Thus trying to communicate and become one with some higher being is not a factor.

The concept of *nowness* plays a very important part. In fact it is of the essence. As a great Tibetan lama, Chogyam Trunpa, once said: "One has to become aware of the present moment through such means as concentrating on one's breathing, a practice that has been developed in the Buddhist tradition. This is based on the knowledge of nowness, for each respiration is unique, is an expression of now."

In *vipassana*, or "meditation insight" practice, you may start by concentrating on the movement of your belly when you take air in and when you exhale; or of the place between your nostrils where you feel each inhalation and each exhalation. Once you have developed a regular discipline of breathing or walking as you stay in the present moment, the technique will die out, and reality will expand.

The first benefit of meditation is that all of life becomes more vivid and enjoyable. It takes on the magnificent hue of some vacations or of special moments in childhood, times in which you proceeded from instant to instant, enjoying the present, and were not constantly distracted inwardly or pestered by thoughts of what you should have said or what you should do tomorrow—that laundry list of things that distract us from experience. Another reason is that meditation may eventually bring you into contact with a larger Reality. We are, after all, small creatures gifted with a consciousness we seldom, if ever, put to full use. Much of our consciousness is educated to verbalize, articulate. But the experiential part of our consciousness is the only part that can actually know greater realities.

There is a limit to the number of techniques we can learn, books we can read, traveling we can do. But there is almost no limit to liberation from the smallness of living on a mundane level, living in local reality, living up to social expectations of what our families want or what pleases our neighbors. Being human we have a thirst for knowledge beyond what we learned in school, knowledge that imbues life with depthless, infinite meaning. To invest ourselves in inner development means liberating ourselves from a drudging, material view of life, a view that life is as we see it on the surface.

To break out of the bubble of ego that divides us from the rest of reality is to enter a kind of consciousness in which we can exist and experience all things. Living becomes awesomely alive; dying takes on a new dimension.

## UNFOLDING MEDITATION

Among the many books on meditation I have found no statements more penetrating than the simple advice given us by Tarthang Tulku in *Gesture of Balance*. Instead of offering more meditative exercises or advice on how to meditate, I quote from this immensely helpful book:

> *Almost all spiritual disciplines practice some form of meditation. Ordinarily, meditation is viewed as a form of thinking about something.*
>
> *Traditionally, beginning meditation involves certain practices such as intense concentration, the visualization of various images, or the chanting of mantras. Teachers emphasize different practices, depending on the needs of the student. A teacher may tell one student to go alone to a quiet place and be completely silent for half an hour to 45 minutes. He may tell another to go to the mountains or ocean and chant very loudly. Someone else may be instructed to gaze at the sky and just be open. Others may be given devotional or ritual partners.*
>
> *Generally, however, our practice should be whatever calms and relaxes us, whatever works best for the development of stillness and concentration. Meditation helps us become calm and happy, enjoy life, be cheerful, and deal effectively with both our physical and mental problems. . . .*

## HOW DO YOU MEDITATE?

First of all, the body must be very still, very quiet. Relax your muscles and let go of all your tension. Then sit in a comfortable position and stay completely still, not moving at all. Breathe very softly and gently. Inhale and exhale slowly and smoothly. As much as you can, completely relax so that your entire nervous system becomes calm.

Then quiet your mind; still your thoughts through inner silence. There are various ways to do this, but too many instructions may be distracting so just very naturally relax your body and pay attention to each breath. The body becomes still, the breath balanced, and the mind and senses very peaceful. You will deeply feel and enjoy your senses coming alive. You can see that meditation is not a difficult task involving something foreign or imported—it is a part of your nature.

There is no need to try to accomplish some goal, since trying itself becomes an obstacle to relaxation. Pushing yourself too hard, or attempting to follow a rigid set of instructions, may cause problems; when you exert too much effort you can find yourself caught between getting something and not getting it, making internal reports to yourself while trying to be silent. When you try to conceptually experience ''perfect meditation,'' you may end up creating endless internal conflicts or inner dialogues.

When you are just learning to meditate, it is best to experience yourself totally, without rejecting or excluding any part of yourself. All your thoughts and feelings can be part of your meditation—you can taste each one, then gradually move on. In this way you can begin to discover the various subtle layers and states of the mind. The mind simply observes its own natural process; every thought, desire and motivation is a natural aid to this basic type of meditation.

When memories or discomforts arise you may feel a little uneasy, but the feeling will pass if you do not mentally hold on to any thought in particular. Just remain very loose and quiet and do not think ''about'' meditation. Simply accept yourself. You are not trying to learn meditation; you *are* the meditation. Your total being—breath, thoughts, senses and awareness—comprises parts of the meditation. You do not have to worry about losing it. Your entire energy-field is a part of the meditation, so you do not need to follow any specific instructions or worry about achieving a particular experience.

As we experience this deeper level of meditation, we find that the nature of the mind is meditation. And that, indeed, is actually the enlightened experience. It is an experience that is free from everything, yet at the same time manifests all and everything.

This itself is liberation.

# BIBLIOGRAPHY

## TRANSITION AND AGING

Ansley, Helen. *Life's Finishing School*. Institute of Noetic Sciences, 1991.

Dychtwald, Kenneth. *The Age Wave*. Jeremy Tarcher, 1990.

Bess, Donovan. *A Practical Guide to Creative Senility*. Blue Dolphin Press, 1988.

Montagu, Ashley. *Growing Young*. McGraw Hill, 1981.

Birren, James, and Diana Woodruff, eds. *Aging*. D. Van Nostrand, 1975.

Benel, Sula. *Abkhasians, the Long Living People of the Caucasus*. Holt, Rinehart & Winston, 1974.

Curtin, Sharon. *Nobody Ever Died of Old Age*. Atlantic Monthly Press, 1972.

## BODY-MIND UNITY FOR HEALTH

Dychtwald, Kenneth. *Bodymind*. Pantheon, 1977.

Keleman, Stanley. *Your Body Speaks Its Mind*. Simon & Schuster, 1975.

Louen, Alexander. *Bioenergetics*. Coward, McCann, 1975.

Brooks, Charles. *Sensory Awareness: The Study of Living as Experience*. Viking Press, 1974.

Geba, Bruno. *Vitality Training for Older Adults*. Random House/Bookworks, 1974.

## RELAXATION

White, John, and James Fadiman, eds. *Relax: How You Can Feel Better.* Dell, 1976.

Benson, Herbert. *The Relaxation Response.* Avon, 1975.


## EXERCISE

Rosenberg, Magda. *Sixty-Plus, Fit Again: Exercises for Older Men and Women.* J. B. Lippincott, 1977.

Bristow, Robert. *Aches and Pains: How the Older Person Can Find Relief Using Heat, Massage, and Exercise.* Pantheon, 1974.

DeVries, Herbert A. *Vigor Regained.* Prentice-Hall, 1974.

Leonard, Jon N., J. L. Hofer and N. Pritikin. *Live, Longer Now—the First 100 Years.* Grosset & Dunlap, 1974.


## YOGA

Brena, S. F. *Pain and Religion.* Charles C. Thomas, 1972.

———. *Yoga and Medicine.* Julian Press, 1972.

Phelan, Nancy, and Michael Volin. *Yoga Over Forty.* Harper & Row, 1965.


## MASSAGE

Carter, Mildred. *The Second Book of Do-In.* Happiness Press, 1976.

———. *Massage and Meditation.* Random House/Bookworks, 1974.

———. *Helping Yourself With Foot Reflexology.* Parker Publishing Co., 1969.

## COMMUNICATION SKILLS AND THERAPY

Cskioszentmihalyi, Mihaly. *Flow, The Psychology of Optimal Experience.* Harper & Row, 1990.

Palmer, Helen. *The Enneagram.* Harper, 1988.

Mindell, Arnold. *Dreambody.* Sigo Press, 1982.

Gordon, Thomas. *Leadership Effectiveness Training.* Wyden Books, 1977.

Rogers, Carl. *On Personal Power.* Delacorte, 1977.

———. *On Becoming a Person.* Houghton Mifflin, 1961.

## VISION AND VISUALIZATION

Samuels, Mike, and Nancy Samuels. *Seeing With the Mind's Eye.* Random House/Bookworks, 1975.

Corbett, Margaret D. *Help Yourself to Better Sight.* Wilshire Book Co., 1974.

## SLEEP AND DREAMS

Delaney, Gayle. *Breakthrough Dreaming.* Bantam Books, 1991.

DeBerge, Stephen. *Lucid Dreaming.* Ballantine, 1985.

Garfield, Patricia. *Creative Dreaming.* Simon and Schuster, 1975.

Faraday, Ann. *Dream Power.* Coward, McCann, 1972.

Luce, G., and J. Segal. *Insomnia.* Doubleday, 1968.

———. *Sleep.* Coward, McCann, 1966.

Jung, Carl. *Memories, Dreams, Reflections.* Recorded and edited by Aniela Jaffee. Pantheon, 1963.

## EXPANDING THE MIND

Houston, Jean. *The Hero and the Goddess: The Odyssey as Myth and Initiation*. Ballantine, 1992.

Catford, Lorna and Michael Ray. *The Path of the Everyday Hero*. Jeremy Tarcher, 1991.

Talbot, Michael. *The Holographic Universe*. Harper Collins, 1991.

Houston, Jean. *The Possible Human*. Jeremy Tarcher, 1982.

Green, Elmer, and Alyce Green. *Beyond Biofeedback*. Delacorte Press/Lawrence, 1978.

Progoff, Ira. *The Well and the Cathedral*. Dialogue House, 1976.

Mishlove, Jeffrey. *The Roots of Consciousness*. Random House/Bookworks, 1975.

Progoff, Ira. *At a Journal Workshop: The Basic Text and Guide for Using the Intensive Journal*. Dialogue House, 1975.

Campbell, Joseph. *The Mythic Image*. Princeton University Press, 1974.

———. *Myths to Live By*. Bantam Books, 1973.

Hayley, Jay. *Uncommon Therapy*. Norton, 1973.

Assagioli, Roberto. *Psychosyntheses*. Viking Press, 1971.

Maslow, Abraham. *The Farther Reaches of Human Nature*. Viking Press, 1971.

Campbell, Joseph. *Hero With a Thousand Faces*. Princeton University Press, 1968.

Maslow, Abraham. *Toward a Psychology of Being*. Van Nostrand Reinhold, 1968.

Erickson, Milton H. *Advanced Techniques of Hypnosis and Therapy*. Jay Haley, ed. Grune & Stratton, 1967.

Watts, Alan. *The Book on the Taboo Against Knowing Who You Are*. Pantheon, 1966.

## DEATH AND DYING

Doore, Gary, ed. *What Survives?* Jeremy Tarcher, 1990.

Feinstein, David and Peg Elliot Mayo. *Rituals for Living and Dying.* Harper, 1990.

Gold, E. J. *The American Book of the Dead.* Gateways/IDHHB, Inc., 1990.

Foos-Greber, Anya. *Deathing.* Nicholas-Hays, 1989.

Levine, Stephen. *Healing Into Life and Death.* Doubleday, 1987.

———. *Meetings at the Edge.* Doubleday, 1984.

Moody, Raymond. *Life After Life.* Bantam Books, 1977.

Kubler-Ross, Elizabeth. *Death the Final Stage of Growth.* Prentice-Hall, 1975.

Keleman, Stanley. *Living Your Dying.* Random House/Bookworks, 1974.

Mannes, Myra. *Last Rights.* William Morrow, 1974.

Kubler-Ross, Elizabeth. *On Death and Dying.* Macmillan, 1968.

## HEALTH AND SELF-HEALING

Chopra, Deepak. *Unconditional Life.* Bantam Books, 1991.

———. *Quantum Healing.* Bantam Books, 1990.

———. *Perfect Health.* Crown, 1990.

Gerrard, Donald. *The Paper Doctor.* Bookworks, 1990.

Reid, Daniel. *The Tao of Health, Sex, and Longevity.* Simon & Schuster, 1989.

Jensen, Bernard. *Beyond Basic Health.* Avery, 1988.

Schwarz, Jack. *It's Not What You Eat But What Eats You.* Celestial Arts, 1988.

Riso, Don Richar. *Personality Types: Using the Enneagram for Self-Discovery.* Houghton Mifflin, 1987.

Miller, Done E. and Julian A. Miller. *Conquest of Aging.* Macmillan, 1986.

Chia, Mantak. *Transform Stress Into Vitality.* Healing Tao Books, 1985.

Weil, Andrew. *Health and Healing.* Houghton Mifflin, 1983.

Hay, Louise. *Heal Your Body.* Hay House, 1982.

Simonton, O. Carl, Stephanie Matthews and James Creighton. *Getting Well Again*. J. P. Tarcher, Inc., 1978.

Pelletier, Kenneth. *Mind As Healer, Mind As Slayer*. Delacorte, 1977.

Shealy, Norman. *Ninety Days to Self-Health*. Dial, 1977.

Ulene, Art. *Feeling Fine*. J. P. Tarcher, Inc., 1977.

Samuels, Mike, and Hal Bennett. *The Well Body Book*. Random House/Bookworks, 1973.

Rogers, Carl R. *On Becoming a Person*. Hougton Mifflin, 1961.

## FOOD AWARENESS AND HEALING

Colbin, Annemarie. *Food and Healing*. Ballantine Books, 1985.

Ornish, Dean. *Stress, Diet, and Your Heart*. Signet, 1984.

Ballantine, Rudolph. *Diet and Nutrition: A Holistic Approach*. Himalayan Institute, 1978.

Lappe, Frances Moore. *Diet for a Small Planet*. Ballantine Books, 1975.

Ornish, Dean. *Nutrition Against Disease*. Bantam Books, 1971.

Bieler, Henry. *Food Is Your Best Medicine*. Vintage Press, 1965.

## SEX

Butler, Robert N., and Myrna I. Lewis. *Sex After Sixty*. Harper & Row, 1976.

Comfort, Alex. *The Joy of Sex*. Crown Publishers, 1972.

## ART AND MUSIC

Luthe, Wolfgang. *The Creativity Mobilization Technique*. Grune & Stratton, 1976.

Bonny, Helen, and Louis Savary. *Music and Your Mind*. Harper & Row, 1973.

## PHILOSOPHY AND MEDITATION

Grof, Christina, and Stanislav Grof. *The Stormy Search for the Self.* J. P. Tarcher, Inc., 1990.

Houston, Jean. *The Search for the Beloved.* J. P. Tarcher, Inc. 1990.

Markides, Kyriacos. *Fire in the Heart.* Paragon House, 1990.

Sandweis, Samuel. *Spirit and the Mind.* Sharada Press, 1985.

Easwaren, Eknath. *Meditation.* Nilgimi Press, 1978.

Schwarz, Jack. *Voluntary Control.* E. P. Dutton, 1978.

Sri, Bhagaran Rajneesh. *Meditation: The Art of Ecstasy.* Harper & Row, 1978.

Thich Nhat Hanh. *The Miracle of Mindfulness.* Beacon Press, 1976.

Tulku, Tarthang. *Gesture of Balance.* Dharma Press, 1976.

Foundation for Inner Peace. *A Course in Miracles.* Foundation for Inner Peace, 1975.

Needleman, Jacob. *The New Religions.* Doubleday, 1975.

Shattuck, E. H. *An Experiment in Mindfulness.* Samuel Weiser, 1972.

Govinda, Anagarika, Lama. *The Way of the White Clouds.* Shambhala, 1970.

Suzuki, Shunryu. *Zen Mind, Beginner's Mind.* John Weatherill, 1970.

Bucke, R. M. *Cosmic Consciousness.* E. P. Dutton, 1969.

Yogananda, Paramahansa. *Autobiography of a Yogi.* Self-Realization Fellowship, 1969.

De Ropp, R. S. *The Master Game.* Dell, 1968.

Shah, Idries. *The Sufis.* Doubleday, 1964.

DeChardin, Teilhard. *The Phenomenon of Man.* Harper & Row, 1959.

Smith, Justin. *The Religions of Man.* Harper & Row, 1958.

Brunton, Paul. *The Secret Path.* E. P. Dutton, 1953.

Huxley, Aldous. *The Perennial Philosophy.* Arno, 1945.

James, William. *The Varieties of Religious Experience.* Modern Library, 1936.

Introducing our new series of Newcastle originals: 'the Living Well Collection'. This creative line of books will provide solid, comprehensive information and advice for people over 50 on lifestyle, finances, relationships, health and fitness, careers, housing, retirement, and much, much more.

**50 & STARTING OVER** . . . . . . . . . . . . . . . . . . . **$10.95**
Career Strategies For Success

**YOUR PERSONAL FITNESS SURVEY** . . . . . . . . **$12.95**
A Guide To Your Current State of Health

**BLUEPRINT FOR SUCCESS** . . . . . . . . . . . . . . . **$12.95**
The Complete Guide to Starting a Business After 50

**LIVING WELL** . . . . . . . . . . . . . . . . . . . . . . . . . **$12.95**
Answers to Life's Practical Mysteries

Spring 1992  **THE FRIENDSHIP BOOK** . . . . . . . . . . . . . . . **$12.95**

Spring 1992  **LONGER LIFE, MORE JOY** . . . . . . . . . . . . . . . **$12.95**

Spring 1992  **WHEN YOUR PARENTS NEED YOU** . . . . . . . . . . . **$9.95**

If you are unable to find any Newcastle book at your local bookstore, please write to:
**Newcastle Publishing Co., Inc.**
13419 Saticoy Street
North Hollywood, CA 91605

INDIVIDUALS: To order any of the books listed in our catalog, please fill out order form, check the number of copies of each title desired, and enclose check or money order for the full amount plus $3.00 postage and handling for the first book ordered; $1.00 for each additional book. Calif. residents please add current sales tax with each order.

**NEWCASTLE PUBLISHING CO., INC.**
P.O. Box 7589, Van Nuys, CA 91409, (213) 873-3191, FAX (818) 780-2007
**VISA AND MASTER CARDS ACCEPTED    $15 MINIMUM ORDER**

Free, complete, current catalogues are available upon request. Just send us your name and address and we will send you a catalogue.
Quantity discounts are available to groups, organizations and companies for any Newcastle title. Telephone (213) 873-3191 or FAX your order to Newcastle Publishing Co., Inc. at (818) 780-2007.

**ORDERS:**                                  Thank you for your interest in Newcastle.
**1-800-932-4809**
                                                    AL SAUNDERS, Publisher